LAPLACE
TRANSFORMATION

Theory and
Engineering Applications

LAPLACE TRANSFORMATION

Theory and Engineering Applications

BY

WILLIAM TYRRELL THOMSON

Professor of Mechanics
University of Wisconsin

New York
PRENTICE-HALL, INC.
1950

Preface

This book covers the theory of Laplace transformation and discusses its application to various problems in engineering and physics. The operational method here refers to the modern approach of functional transformation where the function in terms of the real variable t or x is transformed to a subsidiary function of the variable s by means of the Laplace integral. The inverse operation is then identified either by the original transformation or, for more complicated functions, by the inversion integral based on complex variables. This procedure is recognized as being mathematically more precise than the somewhat ambiguous approach of symbolic algebra as used by Heaviside.

Considerable thought has been given to the organization of the material for simplicity of mathematical development. The idea of functional transformation and its inverse is introduced in the first few pages of the book so that the reader will recognize its procedure and its utility from the beginning. The versatility of the method is greatly increased by the introduction of the unit functions and several theorems in the second chapter. The third and fourth chapters deal with the various applications to problems involving ordinary differential equations. Wherever possible, physical interpretation of the solution is given.

To obtain further insight into the method of Laplace transformation, a chapter on the theory of complex variables is introduced. In it the arguments necessary for the understanding of the inversion integral processes are presented.

The remaining chapters deal with somewhat more advanced problems. In Chapter 6, problems involving partial differential equations are taken up with an emphasis on the procedure of the inversion integral. Iterated transforms are also discussed in relation to such problems.

Chapter 7 is included to illustrate the applicability of Laplace transformation to difference equations. The problems dealt with are, however, of a simpler variety involving only one space coordinate. Transients in such a system are not considered.

One important field for which the Laplace transformation has been rather thoroughly developed is that of the closed-loop systems discussed in Chapter 8. The brief treatment of this chapter is sufficient for the reader to obtain an introductory knowledge of such systems and their stability.

The closing chapter discusses the two types of analogies frequently used in analysis. It should be evident that analogies provide a means of expressing mixed systems in terms of a single system, be they electrical, mechanical, or acoustical.

In keeping with the aims of applied mathematics, a balance between rigor and physical insight has been sought. It is hoped that the book is written in such a way to stimulate further interest in the use of Laplace transformation.

For their influence on the material selected for the book, the writer is indebted to the many authors of texts and papers dealing with the subject of Laplace transformation. Acknowledgement of appreciation is also due to Mr. Gerald H. Cohen, now with the Taylor Instrument Co., who assisted in gathering material for the course in Laplace transformation offered by the Mechanics Department, and to Professor Thomas J. Higgins of the Electrical Engineering Department for his valuable suggestions and criticisms.

WILLIAM TYRRELL THOMSON

Contents

vii

CHAPTER 1

Introduction to the Laplace Transformation

Introduction. The term "operational method" implies a procedure of solving differential equations whereby the boundary or initial conditions are automatically satisfied in the course of the solution. Much of the interest in the operational method was stimulated by Oliver Heaviside (1850–1925) who developed its earlier concepts and applied them successfully to problems dealing with almost every phase of physics and applied mathematics.[1-2] In spite of his notable contributions, Heaviside's development of the operational calculus was largely empirical and lacking in mathematical rigor.

The operational method was placed on a sound mathematical foundation through the efforts of many men. Bromwich[3] and Wagner[4] (1916) were among the first to justify Heaviside's work on the basis of contour integration. Carson[5,6] followed by formulating the operational calculus on the basis of the infinite integral of the Laplace type. The methods of Carson and Bromwich were linked together by Levy[7] and March[8] as two phases of the more general approach. Van der Pol,[9] Doetsch,[10] and others contributed by summarizing the earlier works into a procedure of solution presently known as the operational method of Laplace transformation.[11]

Problems involving ordinary differential equations can be solved operationally by an elementary knowledge of the Laplace transformation, whereas other problems leading to partial differential equations require some knowledge of the complex variable theory for thorough understanding. The study of the complex-variable basis of the operational method is strongly urged, since it offers a more general approach covering cases for which the elementary method is frequently inadequate.

The operational method of Laplace transformation offers a very powerful technique for the fields of applied mathematics. In con-

---

[1-11] Figures refer to titles in Appendix H, Bibliography.

trast to the classical method, which requires the general solution to be fitted to the initial or boundary conditions, these conditions are automatically incorporated in the operational solution for any arbitrary or prescribed excitation. Solutions for impulsive types of excitation and excitation of arbitrary nature can be concisely written operationally. In some cases it is possible to determine the behavior of the system merely by examining the operational equation without actually carrying out the solution.

Special fields to which the operational method can be extended include difference equations, integral equations, and nonlinear equations. Of these, only the simpler phases of difference equations are discussed in this book.

1. Definition of the Laplace Transformation. If $f(t)$ is a known function of t for values of $t > 0$, its Laplace transform $\bar{f}(s)$ is defined by the equation

$$\bar{f}(s) = \int_0^\infty e^{-st} f(t)\, dt \tag{1.1}$$

and abbreviated as

$$\bar{f}(s) = \mathcal{L}f(t) \tag{1.2}$$

As to the limitations on the character of the function $f(t)$ and the allowable range of the variable s, for the present we shall merely state that s must be sufficiently large to make the integral (1.1) convergent.*

EXAMPLE 1.1: Let $f(t) = 1$ for $t > 0$. Then its Laplace transform is

$$\bar{f}(s) = \int_0^\infty e^{-st}\, dt = -\left. \frac{e^{-st}}{s} \right]_0^\infty = \frac{1}{s}$$

which is convergent for all positive s.

EXAMPLE 1.2: Consider the function $f(t) = e^{at}$. Then its Laplace transform is

$$\bar{f}(s) = \int_0^\infty e^{-st} e^{at}\, dt = \int_0^\infty e^{-(s-a)t}\, dt = \frac{1}{s-a}$$

which exists for all s greater than a.

2. Existence Conditions. A sufficient condition for the existence of the Laplace transform of $f(t)$ is evident from EXAMPLE 1.2 Since:

---

* An integral $\int_0^\infty \phi(t)\, dt$ is said to converge if the limit $\lim_{a \to \infty} \int_0^a \phi(t)\, dt$ exists.

the integral

$$\int_0^\infty e^{-(s-a)t}\,dt \tag{2.1}$$

exists for $s > a$, the Laplace transform exists for all functions $f(t)$ satisfying the inequality

$$|e^{-st}f(t)| < C\,e^{-(s-a)t} \tag{2.2}$$

where C is a constant. This is equivalent to stating that $f(t)$ does not grow more rapidly than $C\,e^{at}$, i.e., that $f(t)$ is of exponential order, and that $\lim\limits_{t\to\infty} e^{-st}f(t) = 0$.

3. Transforms of Simple Functions. The Laplace transform of simple functions can be determined by direct integration or integration by parts. Later we shall develop other methods for the evaluation of the transform.

The function $f(t)$ and its transform $\bar{f}(s)$ represent a function-transform pair which can be conveniently tabulated as in Table I.

TABLE I
A Short Table of Function-Transform Pairs

$f(t)$	$\bar{f}(s)$
1	$\dfrac{1}{s}$
t	$\dfrac{1}{s^2}$
e^{at}	$\dfrac{1}{s-a}$
$\sin \omega t$	$\dfrac{\omega}{s^2+\omega^2}$
$\cos \omega t$	$\dfrac{s}{s^2+\omega^2}$

We shall now offer some theorems which will be helpful in the evaluation of transforms.

Linearity Theorem 1: The Laplace transformation is a linear transformation for which superposition holds. For instance, we have from the integral definition of the Laplace transformation the relation $\mathcal{L}cf(t) = c\bar{f}(s)$, where c is a constant. It then follows that

$$\mathcal{L}[c_1 f_1(t) + c_2 f_2(t)] = c_1\bar{f}_1(s) + c_2\bar{f}_2(s)$$

EXAMPLE 3.1:

$$\mathcal{L} \sin \omega t = \mathcal{L}\left(\frac{e^{i\omega t} - e^{-i\omega t}}{2i}\right) = \frac{1}{2i}\left(\frac{1}{s - i\omega} - \frac{1}{s + i\omega}\right) = \frac{\omega}{s^2 + \omega^2}$$

First Shifting Theorem 2: If $\bar{f}(s)$ is the Laplace transform of $f(t)$, then $\bar{f}(s - a)$ is the Laplace transform of $e^{at}f(t)$.

The proof of this theorem follows immediately from the definition of the Laplace transform.

$$\int_0^\infty e^{-st} e^{at}f(t)\ dt = \int_0^\infty e^{-(s-a)t}f(t)\ dt = \bar{f}(s - a) \tag{3.1}$$

This equation is referred to as the shifting theorem in the *s*-plane, since the multiplication of the function by e^{at} shifts the transform of the original function by a.

EXAMPLE 3.2: Find $\mathcal{L}t\ e^{-at}$.

The transform $f(s)$ of t is $1/s^2$, and hence by Theorem 2 we obtain the new transform

$$\mathcal{L}t\ e^{-at} = \frac{1}{(s + a)^2} = -\frac{d}{da}\mathcal{L}\ e^{-at}$$

EXAMPLE 3.3: If $\bar{f}(s) = \mathcal{L}f(t)$, find $\mathcal{L}f(t) \cos \omega t$. Replacing $\cos \omega t$ by $\frac{1}{2}(e^{i\omega t} + e^{-i\omega t})$ and using Theorem 2, we arrive at the result

$$\mathcal{L}f(t) \cos \omega t = \frac{1}{2}[\bar{f}(s - i\omega) + \bar{f}(s + i\omega)] = \Re\bar{f}(s + i\omega)$$

where $\Re$ stands for the real part of the quantity.

Problems

Obtain the following transformations:

1. $\mathcal{L}t = \dfrac{1}{s^2}$

2. $\mathcal{L} \cos \omega t = \dfrac{s}{s^2 + \omega^2}$

3. $\mathcal{L} \sinh \omega t = \dfrac{\omega}{s^2 - \omega^2}$

4. $\mathcal{L} \cosh \omega t = \dfrac{s}{s^2 - \omega^2}$

5. $\mathcal{L}e^{-\alpha t} \sin \omega t = \dfrac{\omega}{(s + \alpha)^2 + \omega^2}$

6. $\mathcal{L}e^{-\alpha t} \cos \omega t = \dfrac{(s + \alpha)}{(s + \alpha)^2 + \omega^2}$

7. $\mathcal{L}t \sin \omega t = \dfrac{2\omega s}{(s^2 + \omega^2)^2}$

8. $\mathcal{L}t \cos \omega t = \dfrac{s^2 - \omega^2}{(s^2 + \omega^2)^2}$

4. Transforms of Derivatives.   *Theorem* 3: If $\lim\limits_{t \to \infty} e^{-st}f(t) = 0$, then $\mathcal{L}f(t) = \bar{f}(s)$ and the Laplace transform of the derivative $f'(t)$

is given by the equation

$$\mathcal{L}f'(t) = s\bar{f}(s) - f(0) \qquad (4.1)$$

To prove this theorem, we integrate by parts and obtain

$$\int_0^\infty e^{-st}f'(t)\,dt = e^{-st}f(t)\Big]_0^\infty + s\int_0^\infty e^{-st}f(t)\,dt$$
$$= -f(0) + s\bar{f}(s)$$

Thus the Laplace transformation reduces the operation of differentiation to a simple algebraic operation of transforms.

To obtain the transform of the second derivative, we proceed as before.

$$\int_0^\infty e^{-st}f''(t)\,dt = e^{-st}f'(t)\Big]_0^\infty + s\int_0^\infty e^{-st}f'(t)\,dt$$

Thus if $\lim\limits_{t\to\infty} e^{-st}f'(t) = 0$, we obtain the equation

$$\mathcal{L}f''(t) = -f'(0) + s\mathcal{L}f'(t)$$
$$= s^2\bar{f}(s) - sf(0) - f'(0) \qquad (4.2)$$

For the transform of the nth derivative, this procedure is repeated n times, the result being

$$\mathcal{L}f^{(n)}(t) = s^n\bar{f}(s) - s^{n-1}f(0) - \cdots - sf^{(n-2)}(0) - f^{(n-1)}(0) \qquad (4.3)$$

Equation (4.3) is valid only if $f(t)$ and all its derivatives through the $(n-1)$st derivative are continuous.*

EXAMPLE 4.1: Find $\mathcal{L}\, t^2/2$.
Letting $f(t) = t^2/2$, we have

$$f(0) = f'(0) = 0$$
$$f''(t) = 1$$

Substituting into Eq. (4.2), we obtain

$$\mathcal{L}1 = \frac{1}{s} = s^2\mathcal{L}\frac{t^2}{2}$$

Therefore
$$\mathcal{L}\frac{t^2}{2} = \frac{1}{s^3}$$

* See Appendix A.

EXAMPLE 4.2: Find $\mathcal{L} \cos \omega t$.

Letting $f(t) = \cos \omega t$, we have

$$f(0) = 1$$
$$f'(0) = 0$$
$$f''(t) = -\omega^2 \cos \omega t$$

Substituting into Eq. 4.2, we obtain

$$-\omega^2 \mathcal{L} \cos \omega t = s^2 \mathcal{L} \cos \omega t - s$$

Therefore
$$\mathcal{L} \cos \omega t = \frac{s}{s^2 + \omega^2}$$

Problems

Obtain the following transforms by the use of the equations of Section 4:

9. $\mathcal{L} \dfrac{t^n}{n!} = \dfrac{1}{s^{n+1}}$

12. $\mathcal{L} \cosh \omega t = \dfrac{s}{s^2 - \omega^2}$

10. $\mathcal{L} \sin \omega t = \dfrac{\omega}{s^2 + \omega^2}$

13. $\mathcal{L} t \sin \omega t = \dfrac{2\omega s}{(s^2 + \omega^2)^2}$

11. $\mathcal{L} \sinh \omega t = \dfrac{\omega}{s^2 - \omega^2}$

14. $\mathcal{L} t \cos \omega t = \dfrac{s^2 - \omega^2}{(s^2 + \omega^2)^2}$

15. Show that the result of Prob. 13 can be obtained by differentiating both sides of the equation $\mathcal{L} \cos \omega t = \dfrac{s}{s^2 + \omega^2}$ with respect to ω.

16. Equation (4.1) is valid only if $f(t)$ is continuous. Show that if $f(t)$ has a finite discontinuity at $t = t_1$, the transform of the first derivative becomes

$$\mathcal{L} f'(t) = s\bar{f}(s) - f(0) - [f(t_1+) - f(t_1-)]e^{-st_1}$$

where $f(t_1+)$ and $f(t_1-)$ are the values of $f(t_1)$ approached from the positive and negative directions, respectively.

5. Transformation of Ordinary Differential Equations. By the application of the Laplace transformation, ordinary differential equations are reduced to algebraic equations of the transform. Consider, for example, the differential equation

$$\frac{d^2y}{dt^2} + \omega^2 y = F(t) \tag{5.1}$$

Applying the Laplace transformation, we obtain

$$s^2\bar{y}(s) - sy(0) - y'(0) + \omega^2\bar{y}(s) = \bar{F}(s)$$

which can be solved for $\bar{y}(s)$ as

$$\bar{y}(s) = \frac{sy(0) + y'(0)}{s^2 + \omega^2} + \frac{\bar{F}(s)}{s^2 + \omega^2} \qquad (5.2)$$

Equation (5.2) is called the *subsidiary equation* of the differential equation (5.1). $\bar{y}(s)$ is the response transform, $\bar{F}(s)$ the driving transform, and $s^2 + \omega^2$ the characteristic function of the system. The first term on the right side of Eq. (5.2), being a function of the initial conditions, is the transform of the transient solution. The second term, which is independent of the initial conditions, represents the transform of the steady-state solution.

For the more general case, the subsidiary equation can be written in the form

$$\bar{y}(s) = \frac{A_1(s)}{B(s)} + \frac{F(s)}{B(s)} \qquad (5.3)$$

where $B(s)$ is the characteristic function and $\bar{y}(s)$ and $\bar{F}(s)$ are the response and driving transforms, respectively.

Problems

Determine the subsidiary equations for the following differential equations:

17. $L\dfrac{di}{dt} + Ri = E, \quad i(0) = 0$

18. $L\dfrac{di}{dt} + Ri = E \sin(\omega t + \varphi)$

19. $\dfrac{d^2y}{dt^2} + 3\dfrac{dy}{dt} + 2y = 0, \quad y(0) = y_0, \quad y'(0) = v_0$

20. $m\dfrac{d^2y}{dt^2} + ky = F$

21. $m\dfrac{d^2y}{dt^2} + c\dfrac{dy}{dt} + ky = F_0 e^{i\omega t}$

6. The Inverse Transformation.   Now that we have determined the subsidiary equation, we must perform an inverse transformation to complete the solution.   This operation, abbreviated as

$$\mathcal{L}^{-1}\bar{f}(s) = f(t) \qquad (6.1)$$

can be performed in some cases by looking up the function $f(t)$ corresponding to the transform $\bar{f}(s)$ in the table of transforms.   This procedure, together with the shifting formula of Theorem 2, is often sufficient for the determination of the inverse transformation.

EXAMPLE 6.1: Find $\mathcal{L}^{-1} \dfrac{1}{(s-a)^2}$.

The inverse transformation of $1/s^2$ is t.   Thus, by Theorem 2,

$$\mathcal{L}^{-1} \frac{1}{(s-a)^2} = t\, e^{at}$$

EXAMPLE 6.2: Find $\mathcal{L}^{-1} \dfrac{s+5}{s^2+2s+5}$.

The given transform can be reduced to the following known form:

$$
\begin{aligned}
\mathcal{L}^{-1} \frac{s+5}{s^2+2s+5} &= \mathcal{L}^{-1} \frac{s+5}{(s+1)^2+4} \\
&= \mathcal{L}^{-1} \frac{s+1}{(s+1)^2+2^2} + 2\mathcal{L}^{-1} \frac{2}{(s+1)^2+2^2} \\
&= e^{-t} \cos 2t + 2\,e^{-t} \sin 2t
\end{aligned}
$$

7. Reduction by Partial Fraction.   In general, the subsidiary equation takes the form

$$\bar{f}(s) = \frac{A(s)}{B(s)} \tag{7.1}$$

For the ordinary differential equation with constant coefficients, $A(s)$ and $B(s)$ are polynomials, the denominator generally being of higher degree than the numerator.   The procedure is then to factor $B(s)$ and express $\bar{f}(s)$ in terms of partial fractions, thereby reducing each term to known form.

EXAMPLE 7.1: Find $\mathcal{L}^{-1} \dfrac{s+1}{s(s^2+s-6)}$.

Factoring the denominator, we can expand in terms of partial fractions.   Let

$$\frac{s+1}{s(s^2+s-6)} = \frac{s+1}{s(s-2)(s+3)} = \frac{C_1}{s} + \frac{C_2}{s-2} + \frac{C_3}{s+3}$$

Reducing the right side to a common denominator, we have, by equating numerators,

$$s + 1 = C_1(s-2)(s+3) + C_2 s(s+3) + C_3 s(s-2)$$

Equating coefficients of like powers of s, we obtain

$$C_1 + C_2 + C_3 = 0$$
$$C_1 + 3C_2 - 2C_3 = 1$$
$$-6C_1 = 1$$

We thus obtain $C_1 = -\frac{1}{6}$, $C_2 = \frac{3}{10}$, and $C_3 = -\frac{2}{15}$. The inverse transform of the given expression is then

$$-\frac{1}{6}\,\mathcal{L}^{-1}\frac{1}{s} + \frac{3}{10}\,\mathcal{L}^{-1}\frac{1}{s-2} - \frac{2}{15}\,\mathcal{L}^{-1}\frac{1}{s+3} = -\frac{1}{6} + \frac{3}{10}\,e^{2t} - \frac{2}{15}\,e^{-3t}$$

8. Transforms Having Simple Poles. We shall now develop a more rapid method of determining the constants C_1, C_2, C_3, $\ldots$ of the partial fraction expansion. Starting with the transform expressed by the quotient of two polynomials

$$\bar{f}(s) = \frac{A(s)}{B(s)} \tag{8.1}$$

where $B(s)$ is of higher degree than $A(s)$ and factorable to n roots a_1, a_2, a_3, $\ldots$, all of which are different, we have

$$B(s) = (s - a_1)(s - a_2)(s - a_3) \cdots (s - a_n) \tag{8.2}$$

The expansion in partial fractions then takes the form

$$\bar{f}(s) = \frac{A(s)}{B(s)} = \frac{C_1}{s - a_1} + \frac{C_2}{s - a_2} + \cdots + \frac{C_n}{s - a_n} \tag{8.3}$$

and we refer to $\bar{f}(s)$ as having n simple or first-order poles, namely, $s = a_1$, a_2, $a_3 \cdots$.

To determine the constant C_k, we multiply both sides of Eq. (8.3) by $(s - a_k)$ and take the limit as $s \to a_k$. This operation results in the equation

$$C_k = \lim_{s \to a_k} \frac{(s - a_k)A(s)}{B(s)} \tag{8.4}$$

Since

$$\mathcal{L}^{-1}\frac{1}{s - a_k} = e^{a_k t}$$

the inverse transformation for the case of simple poles becomes

$$f(t) = \sum_{k=1}^{n} \lim_{s \to a_k} (s - a_k)\bar{f}(s)\, e^{st} \tag{8.5}*$$

* For those familiar with complex-variable theory, Eq. (8.5) is the sum of residues for the case of simple poles.

By the use of complex variables, we shall show in Chapter 5 that Eq. (8.5) also holds for $\bar{f}(s)$ other than polynomials, provided it has only simple poles.

EXAMPLE 8.1: Using Eq. (8.4), verify the numerical values of the coefficients C_1, C_2, and C_3 of Example 7.1.

Writing $\bar{f}(s)$ in the form

$$\bar{f}(s) = \frac{A(s)}{B(s)} = \frac{s+1}{s(s-2)(s+3)}$$

we identify the poles as 0, 2, and -3. Substituting into Eq. (8.4), we obtain

$$C_1 = \lim_{s \to 0} \frac{s+1}{(s-2)(s+3)} = -\frac{1}{6}$$

$$C_2 = \lim_{s \to 2} \frac{s+1}{s(s+3)} = \frac{3}{10}$$

$$C_3 = \lim_{s \to -3} \frac{s+1}{s(s-2)} = -\frac{2}{15}$$

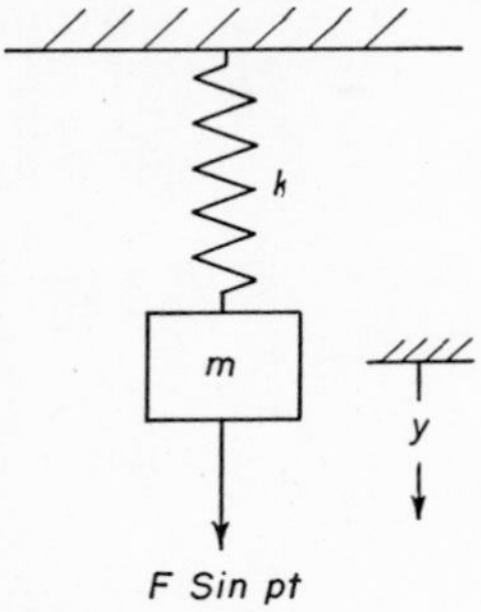

EXAMPLE 8.2: The differential equation for the system shown in Fig. 1 is

F Sin pt

FIG. 1

$$\frac{d^2y}{dt^2} + \omega^2 y = \frac{F}{m} \sin pt$$

where $\omega = \sqrt{k/m}$ is the natural frequency of the system. Determine the solution for the initial conditions $y(0) = y'(0) = 0$ and $p \neq \omega$.

The transform for this case is

$$\bar{y}(s) = \frac{F}{m} \frac{p}{(s^2 + \omega^2)(s^2 + p^2)} = \frac{F}{m} \frac{p}{(s + i\omega)(s - i\omega)(s + ip)(s - ip)}$$

By use of Eq. (8.5), the solution becomes

$$y(t)$$
$$= \frac{F}{m} \left[\frac{p \, e^{i\omega t}}{2i\omega(p^2 - \omega^2)} - \frac{p \, e^{-i\omega t}}{2i\omega(p^2 - \omega^2)} + \frac{p \, e^{ipt}}{2ip(\omega^2 - p^2)} - \frac{p \, e^{-ipt}}{2ip(\omega^2 - p^2)} \right]$$
$$= \frac{F}{m\omega^2[1 - (p/\omega)^2]} \left(\sin pt - \frac{p}{\omega} \sin \omega t \right)$$

Problems

Determine the following inverse transforms:

22. $\mathcal{L}^{-1} \dfrac{s-1}{s(s+2)} = -\dfrac{1}{2} + \dfrac{3}{2} e^{-2t}$

23. $\mathcal{L}^{-1} \dfrac{1}{(s-a)(s-b)} = \dfrac{1}{a-b}(e^{at} - e^{bt})$

24. $\mathcal{L}^{-1} \dfrac{1}{s(s^2+a^2)} = \dfrac{1}{a^2}(1 - \cos at)$

25. $\mathcal{L}^{-1} \dfrac{s+c}{(s+a)(s+b)} = \dfrac{(c-a)e^{-at} - (c-b)e^{-bt}}{(b-a)}$

26. Determine the solution of Prob. 17.

27. Determine the subsidiary equation of the differential equation

$$\frac{d^2y}{dt^2} + \omega^2 y = 0$$

and obtain the solution for $y(0) = y_0$ and $y'(0) = v_0$.

28. Determine the solution for the differential equation

$$\frac{d^2y}{dt^2} + \omega^2 y = F_0$$

for the initial conditions $y(0) = y'(0) = 0$.

29. Prove that Eq. (8.4) can be written as

$$C_k = \frac{A(a_k)}{B'(a_k)}$$

where $B'(s) = \dfrac{d}{ds} B(s)$. *Hint:* First method. Let $B(s) = (s - a_k)B_1(s)$, differentiate with respect to s and let $s \to a_k$. Second method. Treat $\dfrac{(s-a_k)A(s)}{B(s)}$ as an indeterminate case $\dfrac{0}{0}$ and apply L'Hospital's rule.

30. Show that if $\bar{f}(s)$ has a simple pole at the origin, Eq. (8.5) reduces to

$$f(t) = \mathcal{L}^{-1} \frac{A(s)}{sB_1(s)} = \frac{A(0)}{B_1(0)} + \sum_{k=2}^{n} \frac{A(a_k)}{a_k B_1'(a_k)} e^{a_k t}$$

This form was first indicated by Heaviside, who referred to it as his *expansion theorem*.

9. Transforms Having Poles of Higher Order. The equations of Section 8 apply only if $\tilde{f}(s)$ has first-order poles, in which case $B(s)$ has no repeating factors. We shall now consider the case where $B(s)$ has repeating factors in its partial fraction expansion. If a factor in $B(s)$ is repeated k times, we say that $\tilde{f}(s)$ has a kth-order pole.

We shall again start with $\tilde{f}(s)$ in the form

$$\tilde{f}(s) = \frac{A(s)}{B(s)} \tag{9.1}$$

where $B(s)$ is a polynomial of higher degree than $A(s)$. On the assumption that there is a kth-order pole at $s = a_1$, $B(s)$ will have the form

$$B(s) = (s - a_1)^k(s - a_2)(s - a_3) \cdots \tag{9.2}$$

and the partial-fraction expansion of $\tilde{f}(s)$ becomes

$$\tilde{f}(s) = \frac{C_{11}}{(s - a_1)^k} + \frac{C_{12}}{(s - a_1)^{k-1}} + \cdots$$
$$+ \frac{C_{1k}}{(s - a_1)} + \frac{C_2}{(s - a_2)} + \frac{C_3}{(s - a_3)} + \cdots \tag{9.3}$$

To obtain the coefficients C_{1n}, we first multiply both sides of the equation by $(s - a_1)^k$:

$$(s - a_1)^k\tilde{f}(s) = C_{11} + (s - a_1)C_{12} + \cdots + (s - a_1)^{k-1}C_{1k}$$
$$+ \frac{(s - a_1)^kC_2}{(s - a_2)} + \cdots \tag{9.4}$$

C_{11} is then obtained from this equation by letting $s = a_1$:

$$C_{11} = [(s - a_1)^k\tilde{f}(s)]_{s=a_1} \tag{9.5}$$

C_{12} is obtained by differentiating Eq. (9.4) with respect to s and substituting $s = a_1$:

$$C_{12} = \left[\frac{d}{ds}(s - a_1)^k\tilde{f}(s)\right]_{s=a_1} \tag{9.6}$$

It is evident, then, that the equation for the nth coefficient becomes

$$C_{1n} = \frac{1}{(n-1)!}\left[\frac{d^{n-1}}{ds^{n-1}}(s - a_1)^k\tilde{f}(s)\right]_{s=a_1} \tag{9.7}$$

The coefficients C_2, C_3, . . . , are evaluated as in the previous section.

Since by the shifting theorem

$$\mathcal{L}^{-1} \frac{1}{(s - a_1)^n} = \frac{t^{n-1}}{(n - 1)!} e^{a_1 t}$$

the inverse transformation of $\tilde{f}(s)$ becomes

$$f(t) = \left[C_{11} \frac{t^{k-1}}{(k - 1)!} + C_{12} \frac{t^{k-2}}{(k - 2)!} + \cdots \right] e^{a_1 t}$$
$$+ C_2 e^{a_2 t} + C_3 e^{a_3 t} + \cdots \quad (9.8)$$

This equation can also be written in the following compact form, which is applicable to $\tilde{f}(s)$ other than polynomials (see Chapter 5):

$$f(t) = \frac{1}{(k - 1)!} \left[\frac{d^{k-1}}{ds^{k-1}} (s - a_1)^k \tilde{f}(s) e^{st} \right]_{s=a_1} + \sum_{i=2}^{n} [(s - a_i) \tilde{f}(s) e^{st}]_{s=a_i}$$
$$(9.9)$$

EXAMPLE 9.1: Find $\mathcal{L}^{-1} \dfrac{s + 2}{(s - 1)^2 s^3}$.

Here we have a second-order pole at $s = 1$ and a third-order pole at $s = 0$, and the transform can be expanded to the form

$$\frac{C_{11}}{(s - 1)^2} + \frac{C_{12}}{(s - 1)} + \frac{C_{21}}{s^3} + \frac{C_{22}}{s^2} + \frac{C_{23}}{s}$$

Using the equations of this section, we have

$$C_{11} = \left[\frac{s + 2}{s^3} \right]_{s=1} = 3$$

$$C_{12} = \left[\frac{d}{ds} \left(\frac{s + 2}{s^3} \right) \right]_{s=1} = \left[\frac{s^3 - 3s^2(s + 2)}{s^6} \right]_{s=1} = -8$$

$$C_{21} = \left[\frac{(s + 2)}{(s - 1)^2} \right]_{s=0} = 2$$

$$C_{22} = \left[\frac{d}{ds} \frac{(s + 2)}{(s - 1)^2} \right]_{s=0} = \left[\frac{(s - 1)^2 - 2(s - 1)(s + 2)}{(s - 1)^4} \right]_{s=0} = 5$$

$$C_{23} = \frac{1}{2} \left[\frac{d^2}{ds^2} \frac{(s + 2)}{(s - 1)^2} \right]_{s=0} = 8$$

Thus the inverse transformation of the given expression is

$$f(t) = (3t - 8)e^t + (t^2 + 5t + 8)$$

10. Note on Complex Algebra. In many cases the poles of the subsidiary equation are complex numbers. We offer in this section a brief review of complex algebra and point out the simplest procedure for the manipulation of complex quantities.

From Demoivre's theorem, we introduce first the well-known relation

$$e^{i\theta} = \cos \theta + i \sin \theta \tag{10.1}$$

which can be verified from the series expansion of the above functions. The quantity $e^{i\theta}$ can be geometrically interpreted as a unit vector making an angle θ with the real axis as shown in Fig. 2(a).

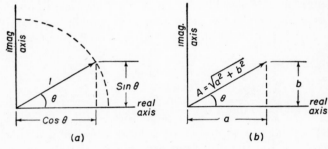

Fig. 2

Thus the complex number $a + ib$ shown in Fig. 2(b) can be represented in the exponential form

$$a + ib = A\, e^{i\theta} \tag{10.2}$$

where $A = \sqrt{a^2 + b^2}$ = amplitude

$\theta = \tan^{-1} \dfrac{b}{a}$ = phase

This result is easily verified by multiplying $a + ib$ by $\sqrt{\dfrac{a^2 + b^2}{a^2 + b^2}}$ as shown:

$$a + ib = \sqrt{a^2 + b^2}\left[\frac{a}{\sqrt{a^2 + b^2}} + i\,\frac{b}{\sqrt{a^2 + b^2}} \right]$$

$$= \sqrt{a^2 + b^2}\,[\cos \theta + i \sin \theta] = A\, e^{i\theta}$$

In general, the manipulation of complex numbers is simpler in the exponential form. The following rules will be found useful.

Multiplication:
$$A_1 e^{i\theta_1} A_2 e^{i\theta_2} = A_1 A_2 e^{i(\theta_1 + \theta_2)} \tag{10.3}$$

Division:
$$\frac{A_1 e^{i\theta_1}}{A_2 e^{i\theta_2}} = \frac{A_1}{A_2} e^{i(\theta_1 - \theta_2)} \tag{10.4}$$

Powers:
$$(A e^{i\theta})^n = A^n e^{in\theta} \tag{10.5}$$

nth Roots:
$$(A e^{i\theta})^{1/n} = A^{1/n} e^{i\theta/n} \tag{10.6}$$

EXAMPLE 10.1: Evaluate $\mathcal{L}^{-1} \dfrac{1}{s^2(s^2 + 2\alpha s + \omega^2)}$.

The given transform can be written in the form

$$\bar{f}(s) = \frac{C_{11}}{s^2} + \frac{C_{12}}{s} + \frac{C_2}{s - s_2} + \frac{C_3}{s - s_3}$$

where the poles are
$$s_1 = 0 = \text{double pole}$$
$$\left. \begin{array}{l} s_2 = -\alpha + i\beta \\ s_3 = -\alpha - i\beta \end{array} \right\} = \left\{ \begin{array}{l} \text{simple poles (conjugate complex} \\ \text{numbers) where } \beta^2 = \omega^2 - \alpha^2 \end{array} \right.$$

The inverse of the above equation is

$$f(t) = C_{11}t + C_{12} + C_2 e^{s_2 t} + C_3 e^{s_3 t}$$

where the C's are to be evaluated. Using the method of Section 9, we have

$$C_{11} = \left(\frac{1}{s^2 + 2\alpha s + \omega^2} \right)_{s=0} = \frac{1}{\omega^2}$$
$$C_{12} = \left[\frac{d}{ds} \left(\frac{1}{s^2 + 2\alpha s + \omega^2} \right) \right]_{s=0} = -\frac{2\alpha}{\omega^4}$$

The constants C_2 and C_3 are evaluated according to the rules for simple poles discussed in Section 8:

$$C_2 = \left[\frac{1}{s^2(s - s_3)} \right]_{s=s_2} = \frac{1}{(-\alpha + i\beta)^2 2i\beta}$$
$$C_3 = \left[\frac{1}{s^2(s - s_2)} \right]_{s=s_3} = \frac{-1}{(-\alpha - i\beta)^2 2i\beta}$$

Here it is advisable to reduce the complex number to the exponential form as follows:

$$(-\alpha + i\beta)^2 = [\sqrt{\alpha^2 + \beta^2}\, e^{i\theta}]^2 = (\alpha^2 + \beta^2)e^{i2\theta}$$

$$\theta = \tan^{-1}\frac{\beta}{-\alpha}$$

$$2\theta = \tan^{-1}\frac{2\alpha\beta}{\beta^2 - \alpha^2}$$

Thus
$$C_2 = \frac{e^{-i2\theta}}{2i\beta(\alpha^2 + \beta^2)}$$

$$C_3 = \frac{-e^{i2\theta}}{2i\beta(\alpha^2 + \beta^2)}$$

Substituting back into the expression for $f(t)$, we obtain

$$f(t) = \frac{t}{\omega^2} - \frac{2\alpha}{\omega^4} + \frac{e^{-i2\theta}e^{(-\alpha+i\beta)t}}{2i\beta(\alpha^2 + \beta^2)} - \frac{e^{i2\theta}e^{(-\alpha-i\beta)t}}{2i\beta(\alpha^2 + \beta^2)}$$

$$= \frac{t}{\omega^2} - \frac{2\alpha}{\omega^4} + \frac{e^{-\alpha t}}{\beta(\alpha^2 + \beta^2)}\left[\frac{e^{i(\beta t - 2\theta)} - e^{-i(\beta t - 2\theta)}}{2i}\right]$$

$$= \frac{t}{\omega^2} - \frac{2\alpha}{\omega^4} + \frac{e^{-\alpha t}}{\beta\omega^2}\sin{(\beta t - 2\theta)}$$

Problems

Determine the following inverse transforms:

31. $\mathcal{L}^{-1}\dfrac{1}{s^2(s + a)} = \dfrac{1}{a^2}(e^{-at} + at - 1)$

32. $\mathcal{L}^{-1}\dfrac{1}{s(s + a)^2} = \dfrac{1}{a^2}[1 - (1 + at)e^{-at}]$

33. $\mathcal{L}^{-1}\dfrac{s + b}{(s + a)^2} = [(b - a)t + 1]e^{-at}$

34. $\mathcal{L}^{-1}\dfrac{1}{(s + a)(s + b)^2} = \dfrac{1}{(a - b)^2}\{e^{-at} + [(a - b)t - 1]e^{-bt}\}$

35. $\mathcal{L}^{-1}\dfrac{1}{s^2(s^2 + \omega^2)} = \dfrac{1}{\omega^3}(\omega t - \sin{\omega t})$

36. $\mathcal{L}^{-1}\dfrac{1}{s^2(s^2 - \omega^2)} = \dfrac{1}{\omega^3}(\sinh{\omega t} - \omega t)$

37. $\mathcal{L}^{-1}\dfrac{s + 2}{(s + 3)(s + 1)^2} = \left(\dfrac{1}{4} + \dfrac{t}{2}\right)e^{-t} - \dfrac{1}{4}e^{-3t}$

38. Solve the differential equation

$$\frac{d^2y}{dt^2} + y = \sin t$$

for $y(0) = 1$ and $y'(0) = -\frac{1}{2}$.

39. Determine the solution for the differential equation

$$\frac{d^2y}{dt^2} + 2\alpha\omega\frac{dy}{dt} + \omega^2 y = F_0$$

for the initial conditions $y(0) = y_0$ and $y'(0) = 0$.

40. Solve the problem of Example 10.1, using Eq. (9.9).

41. In the case where there is a pair of conjugate poles on the imaginary axis, the transform can be written in the form

$$\bar{f}(s) = \frac{A(s)}{(s^2 + \omega^2)B_1(s)}$$

Show that the inverse transform of the above is

$$f(t) = \frac{A(i\omega)e^{i\omega t}}{2i\omega B_1(i\omega)} + \frac{A(-i\omega)e^{-i\omega t}}{-2i\omega B_1(-i\omega)} + \sum_k \frac{A(a_k)e^{a_k t}}{(a_k^2 + \omega^2)B_1'(a_k)}$$

CHAPTER 2

Properties of the Laplace Transformation

Now that the operational method of solution has been introduced, it is advisable at this point to discuss several theorems helpful in carrying out and interpreting the solution. In this chapter we shall also discuss certain operation artifices which enhance the conciseness of the operational method.

11. Initial- and Final-Value Theorems. Certain properties of the Laplace transformation dealing with initial and final values are summarized in the following theorems.

Initial-Value Theorem 4: If $f(t)$ and $f'(t)$ are Laplace transformable, then the behavior of $f(t)$ in the neighborhood of $t = 0$ corresponds to the behavior of $s\bar{f}(s)$ in the neighborhood of $s = \infty$. Expressed mathematically,

$$\lim_{s \to \infty} s\bar{f}(s) = \lim_{t \to 0} f(t) \tag{11.1}$$

To prove this theorem, we start with the equation for the transform of a derivative $f'(t)$:

$$\int_0^\infty e^{-st} f'(t) \, dt = s\bar{f}(s) - f(0)$$

If s is to approach infinity, the normal procedure will be to integrate the left member and then let $s \to \infty$. However, since s is only a parameter and not a function of t, and since the existence of the integral is implied by the theorem on derivatives, we can let $s \to \infty$ before integrating. It is obvious, then, that the left side of the equation is zero, which leads to

$$0 = \lim_{s \to \infty} [s\bar{f}(s) - f(0)]$$

or

$$\lim_{s \to \infty} s\bar{f}(s) = \lim_{t \to 0} f(t)$$

This theorem enables one to determine the behavior of a system in the neighborhood of $t = 0$ from the subsidiary equation without actually carrying out the solution.

18

Final-Value Theorem 5: If $f(t)$ and $f'(t)$ are Laplace transformable and the limit of $f(t)$ as $t \to \infty$ exists, then the behavior of $f(t)$ in the neighborhood of $t = \infty$ corresponds to the behavior of $s\bar{f}(s)$ in the neighborhood of $s = 0$:

$$\lim_{s \to 0} s\bar{f}(s) = \lim_{t \to \infty} f(t) \tag{11.2}$$

To prove this theorem, we start as in Theorem 4 with the expression for the transform of a derivative:

$$\int_0^\infty e^{-st} f'(t)\, dt = s\bar{f}(s) - f(0)$$

Using the same argument as in the previous theorem, we allow $s \to 0$ before integrating, and the left side of the equation becomes

$$\int_0^\infty f'(t)\, dt = \lim_{t \to \infty} \int_0^t f'(t)\, dt = \lim_{t \to \infty} [f(t) - f(0)]$$

Equating this to the right side of the previous equation, we obtain

$$\lim_{t \to \infty} [f(t) - f(0)] = \lim_{s \to 0} [s\bar{f}(s) - f(0)]$$

Since $f(0)$ is not a function of t or s, the quantity $f(0)$ cancels from the above equation, leaving the result

$$\lim_{s \to 0} s\bar{f}(s) = \lim_{t \to \infty} f(t)$$

It should be pointed out that this theorem cannot be applied to oscillating functions such as $\sin \omega t$, since $\sin \infty$ does not have a definite value; that is, the restrictions on $\bar{f}(s)$ require that its roots lie to the left of the imaginary axis of the s-plane.

EXAMPLE 11.1: Determine the initial and final velocities of a mass m which is allowed to fall through a column of oil.

Assuming the resistance offered by the oil to be proportional to the velocity of m, the differential equation of motion written in terms of the velocity is

$$m \frac{dv}{dt} = -cv + mg$$

where c is the coefficient of viscous damping and g is the gravitational acceleration. Upon application of the Laplace transformation, the subsidiary equation becomes

$$m[s\bar{v}(s) - v(0)] = -c\bar{v}(s) + \frac{mg}{s}$$

$$\bar{v}(s) = \frac{mg}{s(ms + c)} + \frac{mv(0)}{(ms + c)}$$

The initial value, from Theorem 4, is

$$\lim_{s \to \infty} s\bar{v}(s) = v(0)$$

and the final value, from Theorem 5, is

$$\lim_{s \to 0} s\bar{v}(s) = \frac{mg}{c}$$

12. Differentiation and Integration. Under certain restrictions the differentiation and integration in the real domain correspond to multiplication and division by s in the subsidiary domain.

Differentiation Theorem 6: If $f(t)$ and $f'(t)$ are Laplace transformable, and if $s\bar{f}(s)$ has a denominator of higher degree than the numerator, then the multiplication of $\bar{f}(s)$ by s corresponds to the differentiation of $f(t)$ with respect to t.

This theorem follows directly from the equation for the Laplace transform of a derivative

$$\mathcal{L}f'(t) = s\bar{f}(s) - f(0)$$

for the case $f(0) = 0$, and we need only to investigate under what condition the initial value $f(0)$ is zero.

Using the initial-value theorem, we have

$$\lim_{t \to 0} f(t) = f(0) = \lim_{s \to \infty} s\bar{f}(s)$$

If $s\bar{f}(s)$ has a denominator of higher power than the numerator, then as $s \to \infty$, $f(0) = 0$, and we obtain the relation

$$s\bar{f}(s) = \mathcal{L}f'(t) \tag{12.1}$$

Integration Theorem 7: If $\mathcal{L}f(t) = \bar{f}(s)$ exists, then the division of $\bar{f}(s)$ by s corresponds to integration of $f(t)$ with respect to t between the limits 0 and t.

To prove this theorem, we have from the definition of the Laplace transform the following equation:

$$\mathcal{L} \int_0^t f(t) \, dt = \int_0^\infty e^{-st} \left[\int_0^t f(t) \, dt \right] dt$$

By making the following substitutions

$$u = \int_0^t f(t)\, dt, \quad dv = e^{-st}\, dt$$

$$du = f(t)\, dt, \qquad v = -\frac{e^{-st}}{s}$$

and integrating by parts, we obtain

$$\pounds \int_0^t f(t)\, dt = -\frac{e^{-st}}{s} \int_0^t f(t)\, dt \Big]_0^\infty + \frac{1}{s} \int_0^\infty e^{-st} f(t)\, dt$$

By substitution of the limits, the first term on the right side of this equation is zero, and we arrive at the result

$$\pounds \int_0^t f(t)\, dt = \frac{1}{s} \int_0^\infty e^{-st} f(t)\, dt = \frac{1}{s} \bar{f}(s) \qquad (12.2)$$

which agrees with the statement of the theorem.

EXAMPLE 12.1: Starting with the transform

$$\pounds t\, e^{-at} = \frac{1}{(s + a)^2}$$

derive a new function-transform pair by using Theorem 6.

The given quantity is $\bar{f}(s) = 1/(s + a)^2$. Thus $s\bar{f}(s) = s/(s + a)^2$, which is a rational fraction with a denominator of higher degree than the numerator. Theorem 6 thus applies, and we obtain the new pair

$$\frac{s}{(s + a)^2} = \pounds \frac{d}{dt} (t\, e^{-at}) = \pounds (1 - at)\, e^{-at}$$

EXAMPLE 12.2: Starting with the transform

$$\pounds \sin \omega t = \frac{\omega}{s^2 + \omega^2}$$

derive a new pair by using Theorem 7.

Substituting into Eq. (12.2), we obtain

$$\frac{\omega}{s(s^2 + \omega^2)} = \pounds \int_0^t \sin \omega t\, dt = \pounds \left[\frac{-\cos \omega t}{\omega} \right]_0^t$$

$$= \pounds \frac{1}{\omega} (1 - \cos \omega t)$$

13. Multiplication and Division by t. Theorems 8 and 9, given without proof, are left for the student to prove. They are the result of performing the indicated operations on the integral definitions of $\bar{f}(s)$.

Theorem 8—Multiplication of $f(t)$ by t: If $\mathcal{L}f(t) = \bar{f}(s)$, then

$$\mathcal{L}tf(t) = -\frac{d}{ds}\bar{f}(s) \tag{13.1}$$

Theorem 9—Division of $f(t)$ by t: If $\mathcal{L}f(t) = \bar{f}(s)$, then

$$\mathcal{L}\frac{f(t)}{t} = \int_s^\infty \bar{f}(s)\,ds \tag{13.2}$$

EXAMPLE 13.1: Determine $\mathcal{L}t \sin \omega t$. Letting $f(t) = \sin \omega t$, we have from Theorem 8 the desired transform

$$\mathcal{L}t \sin \omega t = -\frac{d}{ds}\left(\frac{\omega}{s^2 + \omega^2}\right) = \frac{2\omega s}{(s^2 + \omega^2)^2}$$

Problems

42. Starting with the transform pair

$$\frac{1}{\omega}\mathcal{L}\,e^{-at}\sin \omega t = \frac{1}{(s + a)^2 + \omega^2}$$

determine the new transform pair resulting from the use of Theorem 6.

43. Starting with

$$\frac{1}{\omega^2}\mathcal{L}(1 - \cos \omega t) = \frac{1}{s(s^2 + \omega^2)}$$

determine the new transform pair resulting from the use of Theorem 7.

44. Starting with the pair

$$\mathcal{L}\,e^{-at} = \frac{1}{s + a}$$

derive the functions corresponding to the transforms

$$\frac{1}{s(s + a)} \quad \text{and} \quad \frac{1}{s^2(s + a)}$$

45. Determine $\mathcal{L}t \sinh \omega t$, starting from the known relation

$$\mathcal{L} \sinh \omega t = \frac{\omega}{s^2 - \omega^2}$$

46. Apply Theorem 9 to

$$\mathcal{L}t \sin \omega t = \frac{2\omega s}{(s^2 + \omega^2)^2}$$

and prove that $\mathcal{L} \sin \omega t = \dfrac{\omega}{s^2 + \omega^2}$

47. Determine the complete solution for Example 11.1 and verify the results given.

48. If a constant force F is applied to the system of Fig. 3, determine the initial and final velocities of the upper end without completing the solution.

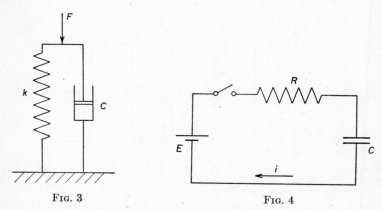

FIG. 3   FIG. 4

49. The capacitor C of Fig. 4 is uncharged at the instant the switch is closed. Determine the subsidiary equation for the current i and find its initial and final values. Verify by completing the solution.

14. The Unit Step Function.

A knowledge of certain basic functions about to be discussed greatly increases the power of the operational method. Of these functions, the unit step function can be considered to be the basic building block. As shown graphically in Fig. 5, the unit step function is zero for $t < a$ and unity for $t > a$. Its transform, by definition, is

$$\mathcal{L}\,\mathcal{U}(t - a) = \int_0^\infty e^{-st}\mathcal{U}(t - a)\,dt = \int_0^a e^{-st}0\,dt$$

$$+ \int_a^\infty e^{-st}1\,dt = \frac{e^{-as}}{s} \quad (14.1)$$

Thus, if $a = 0$ we have the special case

$$\mathcal{L}\,\mathfrak{U}(t) = \frac{1}{s} \tag{14.2}$$

Any function $f(t)$ multiplied by $\mathfrak{U}(t - a)$ will have a value of zero for $t < a$ and $f(t)$ in the region $t > a$.

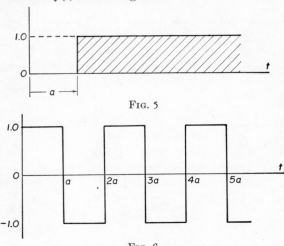

Fig. 5

Fig. 6

Example 14.1: Express the square wave shown in Fig. 6 in terms of the unit step function, and obtain its Laplace transform.

By adding and subtracting step functions started at a, $2a$, $3a$, . . . , we can express the square wave of Fig. 6 by the equation

$$f(t) = \mathfrak{U}(t) - 2\mathfrak{U}(t - a) + 2\mathfrak{U}(t - 2a) - 2\mathfrak{U}(t - 3a)$$
$$+ 2\mathfrak{U}(t - 4a) \cdots$$

Its transform is obtained by substituting from Eq. (14.1):

$$\bar{f}(s) = \frac{1}{s} - 2\frac{e^{-as}}{s} + 2\frac{e^{-2as}}{s} - 2\frac{e^{-3as}}{s} + \cdots$$

$$= \frac{1}{s}\,[1 - 2e^{-as}(1 - e^{-as} + e^{-2as} - e^{-3as} + \cdots)]$$

$$= \frac{1}{s}\left(1 - \frac{2e^{-as}}{1 + e^{-as}}\right) = \frac{1}{s}\left(\frac{1 - e^{-as}}{1 + e^{-as}}\right)$$

$$= \frac{1}{s}\,\tanh\frac{as}{2}$$

This equation is sometimes referred to as the *meander function*.

15. The Unit Impulse. By combining two step functions of height $1/c$ as shown in Fig. 7 and approaching a limit as $c \to 0$, we obtain another important quantity known as the *unit impulse*. Expressed mathematically, the unit impulse is given by the following limit:

$$\mathcal{U}'(t - a) = \lim_{c \to 0} \left[\frac{1}{c} \mathcal{U}(t - a) - \frac{1}{c} \mathcal{U}(t - a - c) \right] \quad (15.1)$$

and it is evident that its value, as shown by the shaded area of Fig. 7, is unity at $t = a$ and zero everywhere else.

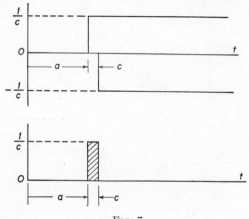

Fig. 7

Its transform can be obtained by substituting Eq. (14.1) in (15.1) and using L'Hospital's rule for the determination of an indeterminate quantity; that is, the numerator and denominator are separately differentiated with respect to c, after which c is allowed to approach zero.

$$\mathcal{L}\mathcal{U}'(t - a) = \lim_{c \to 0} \left[\frac{e^{-as} - e^{-(a+c)s}}{cs} \right] = e^{-as} \quad (15.2)$$

Comparison of Eq. (14.1) with (15.2) indicates that the unit impulse is the time rate of change of the unit function (see Theorem 6), which explains the notation adopted. Among physicists, the unit impulse is referred to as the "Dirac-δ function."

The unit impulse has many applications, the most obvious of which is implied by the name. Consider an impulse of magnitude

I_0 lb-sec applied to a system at $t = a$. Keeping I_0 constant, we can consider this impulse to be the limiting case of a force of I_0/c lb acting for a time duration of c sec as c approaches zero. As shown in Fig. 8, the impulsive force F_i in the limiting case becomes equal to

$$F_i = \lim_{c \to 0} \frac{I_0}{c} [\mathfrak{u}(t - a) - \mathfrak{u}(t - a - c)] = I_0 \mathfrak{u}'(t - a) \quad (15.3)$$

and its transform is

$$\mathcal{L} I_0 \mathfrak{u}'(t - a) = I_0 e^{-as} \quad (15.4)$$

Thus the response of a system to an impulse is obtained by using an impulsive force $F_i = I_0 \mathfrak{u}'(t - a)$ in the differential equation of

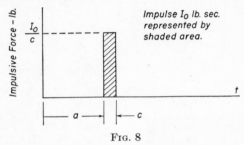

Fig. 8

force. It should be noted here that $I_0 \mathfrak{u}'(t - a)$ must have the dimensions of a force; hence $\mathfrak{u}'(t - a)$ must have the dimensions of time^{-1}. This is evident from the fact that $\mathfrak{u}(t - a)$ is non-dimensional and $\mathfrak{u}'(t - a)$ is the derivative of $\mathfrak{u}(t - a)$.

Another interesting application of the unit impulse is found in the representation of a concentrated force by the limiting case of a loading in force per unit area or force per linear dimension. In this case, the time coordinate t is replaced by a space coordinate x.

Consider a case in which it is desired to write a loading equation corresponding to a concentrated force P lb acting at a position $x = a$ on a beam. On the assumption that the force is replaced by a distributed load of P/c lb/in. acting over a length c, the limiting case of the loading w_p lb/in. as $c \to 0$ is

$$w_p = \lim_{c \to 0} \frac{P}{c} [\mathfrak{u}(x - a) - \mathfrak{u}(x - a - c)] = P \mathfrak{u}'(x - a) \quad (15.5)$$

Thus $P \mathfrak{u}'(x - a)$ is the loading (lb/in.) corresponding to a concentrated load P lb acting at $x = a$.

16. The Unit Doublet. The unit doublet $\mathcal{U}''(t - a)$ shown graphically in Fig. 9 is defined by the limit

$$\mathcal{U}''(t - a)$$
$$= \lim_{c \to 0} \left[\frac{\mathcal{U}(t - a) - 2\mathcal{U}(t - a - c) + \mathcal{U}(t - a - 2c)}{c^2} \right] \quad (16.1)$$

The shaded area of Fig. 9 is readily obtained by combining three step functions as indicated by Eq. (16.1).

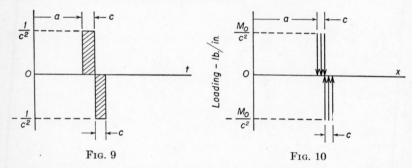

FIG. 9   FIG. 10

Its transform can be obtained by substituting Eq. (14.1) in (16.1) and allowing c to approach zero:

$$\mathcal{L}\mathcal{U}''(t - a) = \lim_{c \to 0} \left[\frac{e^{-as} - 2e^{-(a+c)s} + e^{-(a+2c)s}}{c^2 s} \right] = s\, e^{-as} \quad (16.2)$$

The above limit is indeterminate to the second order, however, and requires two applications of L'Hospital's rule; that is, the numerator and denominator must be differentiated separately with respect to c two times.

Comparison of Eq. (15.2) with (16.2) indicates that the unit doublet is the time rate of change of the unit impulse. Interpreted graphically, the shaded area of Fig. 9 represents a couple of unit magnitude.

EXAMPLE 16.1: If at a given position $x = a$ on a structure a mechanical couple of moment M_0 is applied, show that the corresponding loading is expressible in terms of the unit doublet.

If we let the couple be represented by the limiting case as $c \to 0$ of distributed loads M_0/c^2 lb/in. applied as shown in Fig. 10, the loading w_M is equal to $M_0 \mathcal{U}''(x - a)$ and its transform is $M_0 s\, e^{-as}$.

It is evident, then, that $\mathfrak{U}''(x - a)$ must have the dimensions of length^{-2}.

17. The Second Shifting Theorem. Shifting of a transform $\bar{f}(s)$ to $\bar{f}(s - a)$ was discussed by the first shifting theorem of Chapter 1. Now we shall discuss shifting in the original plane, that is, $f(x)$ to $f(x - a)$.

Theorem 10: If the inverse transformation of $\bar{f}(s)$ is $f(x)$, then the inverse transformation of $e^{-as}\bar{f}(s)$ is $f(x - a)\mathfrak{U}(x - a)$:

$$\mathcal{L}^{-1} e^{-as}\bar{f}(s) = f(x - a)\mathfrak{U}(x - a) \tag{17.1}$$

For the proof of this theorem, we start with the definition of Laplace transformation:

$$\bar{f}(s) = \int_0^\infty e^{-s\lambda} f(\lambda) \, d\lambda$$

Letting $\lambda = (x - a)$,

$$\bar{f}(s) = \int_a^\infty e^{-s(x-a)} f(x - a) \, dx = e^{as} \int_a^\infty e^{-sx} f(x - a) \, dx$$

$$= e^{as} \int_0^\infty e^{-sx} f(x - a)\mathfrak{U}(x - a) \, dx \tag{17.2}$$

Therefore
$$e^{-as}\bar{f}(s) = \int_0^\infty e^{-sx} f(x - a)\mathfrak{U}(x - a) \, dx \tag{17.3}$$

$$\mathcal{L}^{-1} e^{-as}\bar{f}(s) = f(x - a)\mathfrak{U}(x - a) \tag{17.4}$$

EXAMPLE 17.1: Evaluate $\mathcal{L}^{-1} e^{-as}/s^3$. Here $\bar{f}(s) = 1/s^3$ and $f(x) = x^2/2!$ Thus from Eq. (17.4),

$$\mathcal{L}^{-1} \frac{e^{-as}}{s^3} = \frac{(x - a)^2}{2!} \mathfrak{U}(x - a)$$

Problems

50. Show that the transform of the function shown in Fig. 11 is

$$\bar{f}(s) = \frac{1}{s(1 + e^{-as})}$$

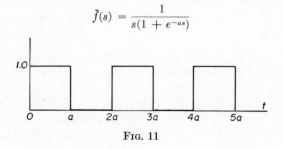

FIG. 11

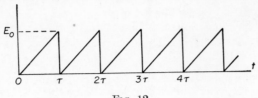

Fig. 12

51. Show that the transform of the saw-tooth wave of Fig. 12 is

$$\bar{f}(s) = E_0 \left[\frac{1}{\tau s^2} - \frac{e^{-\tau s}}{s(1 - e^{-\tau s})} \right]$$

52. The differential equation for the loading on a uniform beam of stiffness EI is

$$EI \frac{d^4y}{dx^4} = \omega(x) \quad \text{lb/in.}$$

Determine the equation for the loading $w(x)$ for the beam shown in Fig. 13.

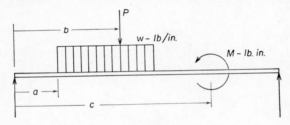

Fig. 13

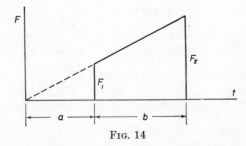

Fig. 14

53. A force varied with time as shown in Fig. 14. Show that its operational expression and its transform are

$$\begin{cases} F(t) = \dfrac{F_1}{a} t[\mathcal{U}(t - a) - \mathcal{U}(t - a - b)] \\[2mm] \bar{F}(s) = \dfrac{F_1}{as^2} \{(1 + as)e^{-as} - [1 + (a + b)s]e^{-(a+b)s}\} \end{cases}$$

54. A pressure pulse p_0 started at one end of a tube of length l travels with speed c to the other end without loss of intensity. If the ratio of the reflected to the incident pulse at each end is r, show that the pressure at any point x in the tube is given by the equation

$$p(t) = p_0 \left[\mathcal{U}'\left(t - \frac{x}{c}\right) + r\mathcal{U}'\left(t - \frac{2l - x}{c}\right) + r^2\mathcal{U}'\left(t - \frac{2l + x}{c}\right) \right.$$
$$\left. + r^3\mathcal{U}'\left(t - \frac{4l - x}{c}\right) + \cdots \right]$$

55. The differential equation for the loading $p(r)$ lb/in.^{2} of a thin circular plate under symmetrical loading is given as

$$D\nabla^4 z = p(r)$$

If a total load P is applied along a circular line of radius a as in Fig. 15, show that

$$p(r) = \frac{P}{2\pi r} \mathcal{U}'(r - a)$$

where r is the radial distance measured from the center of the plate.

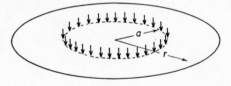

Fig. 15

18. Periodic Functions. If a function $f(t)$ is periodic, then $f(t) = f(t + \tau)$, where τ is the period. Its transform can be written

$$\bar{f}(s) = \int_0^\infty e^{-st}f(t)\, dt = \int_0^\tau e^{-st}f(t)\, dt + \int_\tau^{2\tau} e^{-st}f(t)\, dt + \cdots \quad (18.1)$$

By use of the second shifting theorem, Eq. (18.1) can be rewritten as

$$\bar{f}(s) = (1 + e^{-\tau s} + e^{-2\tau s} + \cdots) \int_0^\tau e^{-st}f(t)\, dt$$
$$= \frac{1}{(1 - e^{-\tau s})} \int_0^\tau e^{-st}f(t)\, dt \quad (18.2)$$

EXAMPLE 18.1: Determine the transform of the half-wave rectification of sin ωt shown in Fig. 16.

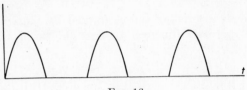

FIG. 16

The period τ is $2\pi/\omega$, and the function is

$$f(t) = \sin \omega t \qquad \left(0 \leq t \leq \frac{\pi}{\omega}\right)$$

$$= 0 \qquad \left(\frac{\pi}{\omega} \leq t \leq \frac{2\pi}{\omega}\right)$$

Thus from Eq. (18.2) we have

$$\bar{f}(s) = \frac{1}{1 - e^{-2\pi s/\omega}} \int_0^{\pi/\omega} e^{-st} \sin \omega t \, dt$$

$$= \frac{1}{1 - e^{-2\pi s/\omega}} \left[\frac{e^{-st}(s \sin \omega t - \omega \cos \omega t)}{s^2 + \omega^2}\right]_0^{\pi/\omega}$$

$$= \frac{\omega(1 + e^{-\pi s/\omega})}{(s^2 + \omega^2)(1 - e^{-2\pi s/\omega})} = \frac{\omega}{(s^2 + \omega^2)(1 - e^{-\pi s/\omega})}$$

19. Pulsed Periodic Functions. First we shall introduce the following theorem, which can be applied to pulses of periodic functions.

Theorem 11: If $f(t)$ is periodic such that $f(t) = f(t + a)$ and $\mathcal{L}f(t) = \bar{f}(s)$, then

$$\mathcal{L}f(t)\mathcal{U}(t - a) = e^{-as}\bar{f}(s) \tag{19.1}$$

For the proof of this theorem we note that $f(t)\mathcal{U}(t - a)$ is zero for $t < a$ and $f(t)$ for $t > a$. Thus

$$\mathcal{L}f(t)\mathcal{U}(t - a) = \int_a^{\infty} e^{-st}f(t) \, dt \tag{19.2}$$

Introducing a new variable $\lambda = t - a$, we have

$$\int_a^{\infty} e^{-st}f(t) \, dt = e^{-as} \int_0^{\infty} e^{-s\lambda}f(\lambda + a) \, d\lambda = e^{-as} \int_0^{\infty} e^{-s\lambda}f(\lambda) \, d\lambda \tag{19.3}$$

Thus we have $\qquad \mathcal{L}f(t)\mathcal{U}(t - a) = e^{-as}\bar{f}(s)$

where a is any integral multiple of the period of $f(t)$.   We note here that this result could have been obtained directly from Theorem 10, since $f(t \pm a) = f(t)$.

Consider next a series of pulses formed by blanking out equal intervals of a periodic function $f(t)$, as shown in Fig. 17.   The

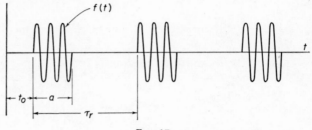

FIG. 17

resulting wave $F(t)$ is then also periodic with a pulse repetition period τ_r, and Eq. (18.2) becomes applicable.

$$\bar{F}(s) = \frac{1}{1 - e^{-\tau_r s}} \int_0^{\tau_r} e^{-st} F(t)\, dt \qquad (19.4)$$

If we use the unit step function for blanking out portions of the period, $F(t)$ for one period becomes

$$F(t) = f(t)[\mathfrak{U}(t - t_0) - \mathfrak{U}(t - t_0 - a)] \qquad (19.5)$$

Hence from Theorem 11 we obtain the transform of the pulse:

$$\bar{F}(s) = \frac{e^{-t_0 s}(1 - e^{-as})\bar{f}(s)}{(1 - e^{-\cdot_r s})} \qquad (19.6)$$

If the origin is chosen so that $t_0 = 0$, then the factor $e^{-t_0 s}$ becomes equal to unity.

EXAMPLE 19.1: A series of pulses are produced by a sinusoidal carrier wave of frequency 1 megacycle per second which is on for 4 cycles with a repetition frequency of 5000 cycles per second. Determine its transform.

For this problem,

$$f(t) = \sin \omega t$$
$$\bar{f}(s) = \frac{\omega}{s^2 + \omega^2}$$

From Eq. (19.6),

$$\bar{F}(s) = \frac{\omega}{s^2 + \omega^2}\left(\frac{1 - e^{-as}}{1 - e^{-\tau_r s}}\right)$$

where

$$\omega = 2\pi \times 10^6 \text{ rad/sec}$$
$$a = 4 \times 10^{-6} \text{ sec}$$
$$\tau_r = 200 \times 10^{-6} \text{ sec}$$

EXAMPLE 19.2: Repeat Example 18.1 by the method of Section 19.

The function $f(t)$ is again sinusoidal and equal to $\sin \omega t$. The pulse interval $a = \pi/\omega$ is, however, equal to only half a period $\tau = 2\pi/\omega$ and $f(t + a) = -f(t)$ [see Eq. (19.3)]. Thus from Eq. (19.6),

$$\bar{F}(s) = \frac{(1 + e^{-as})\bar{f}(s)}{(1 - e^{-\tau s})}$$
$$= \frac{\omega}{s^2 + \omega^2}\left(\frac{1 + e^{-\pi s/\omega}}{1 - e^{-2\pi s/\omega}}\right)$$

Problems

56. The full-wave rectification of the $\sin \omega t$ curve can be obtained by the addition of the curve of Fig. 16 and the same curve shifted to the right by π/ω. Show that its transform is

$$\bar{f}(s) = \frac{\omega}{s^2 + \omega^2} \coth \frac{\pi s}{2\omega}$$

57. Solve Probs. 50 and 51 by the use of Eq. (18.2).

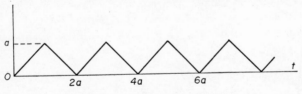

FIG. 18

58. Show that the transform of the function shown in Fig. 18 is

$$\bar{f}(s) = \frac{1}{s^2} \tanh \frac{as}{2}$$

59. Figure 19 shows a series of sinusoidal pulses with a repetition period of 4 microseconds. Show that its transform is

$$\bar{F}(s) = \frac{1}{2}\left[\frac{4\pi}{s^2 + (4\pi)^2}\right]\frac{1}{\cosh s}$$

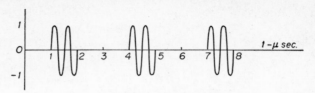

FIG. 19

60. Figure 20 shows a series of damped oscillations $f(t) = e^{-\alpha t} \sin \omega t$ repeated every τ sec.   Assuming that α is large enough that $f(\tau) = 0$, show

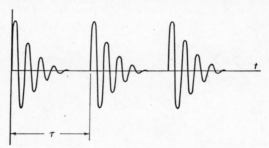

FIG. 20

that its transform is

$$\bar{F}(s) = \left[\frac{\omega}{(s + \alpha)^2 + \omega^2} \right] \frac{1}{(1 - e^{-\tau s})}$$

20. Indicial Response.   The indicial response $g(t)$ is defined as the responses of a system to a unit step function.   For instance, the response transform $\bar{g}(s)$ to a unit step function can be written

$$\bar{g}(s) = \frac{1}{sZ(s)} \tag{20.1}$$

where $Z(s)$ is the system or impedance transform and $1/s$ is the transform of $\mathcal{U}(t)$.   The indicial response is then

$$g(t) = \mathcal{L}^{-1} \frac{1}{sZ(s)} \tag{20.2}$$

The term "indicial response" (or "indicial admittance") was originally adopted in connection with electric circuit theory as the response of a system to a unit steady voltage; for instance, the current in some portion of the circuit due to the switching in of a battery.   This would correspond in the mechanical system to the sudden application of a steady force, a condition which is much more difficult to realize physically.

EXAMPLE 20.1: Determine the indicial response of a series RL circuit.

The differential equation for the current in the circuit with a unit voltage applied at $t = 0$ is

$$L \frac{di}{dt} + Ri = \mathfrak{u}(t)$$

With the initial current equal to zero, the subsidiary equation becomes

$$\bar{\imath}(s) = \frac{1}{Ls(s + R/L)}$$

The indicial response which is the inverse transformation of the above equation is then

$$g(t) = i(t) = \frac{1}{R} (1 - e^{-\frac{R}{L}t})$$

21. Impulsive Response.   The response of a system to a unit impulse is a quantity of fundamental importance.

Using the notation $h(t)$ and $\bar{h}(s)$ for the impulsive response and its transform, we can write

$$\bar{h}(s) = \frac{1}{Z(s)} \tag{21.1}$$

$$h(t) = \mathcal{L}^{-1} \frac{1}{Z(s)} \tag{21.2}$$

where $Z(s)$ is again the impedance transform and 1 is the transform of $\mathfrak{u}'(t)$.   As will be shown in Section 22, the importance of this quantity is linked with the fact that the response of a system to any arbitrary excitation can be directly expressed in terms of the impulsive response through the convolution integral.

EXAMPLE 21.1: Determine the impulsive response of a spring-mass system of Fig. 21.

The problem resolves into one of finding the response of the system when an impulse of unit magnitude is applied to m.   From

Eq. (15.3), the impulsive force for $I_0 = 1$ lb-sec is $\mathfrak{U}'(t)$.   Thus the differential equation becomes

$$m\frac{d^2x}{dt^2} + kx = \mathfrak{U}'(t)$$

Since the corresponding subsidiary equation is

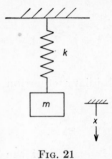

$$\bar{x}(s) = \frac{1}{m\left(s^2 + \dfrac{k}{m}\right)}$$

the impulsive response from its inverse becomes

$$h(t) = x(t) = \frac{1}{\sqrt{km}}\sin\sqrt{\frac{k}{m}}\,t$$

We note that this equation is dimensionally correct if we remember that the quantity 1 in the numerator is impulse (lb-sec) and $\sqrt{km}$ is impedance (force/velocity).

FIG. 21

22. The Convolution Integral.   Given the impulsive response $h(t)$ of a system, it is possible to determine the response of the

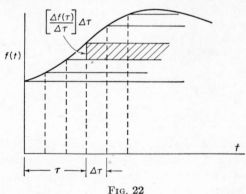

FIG. 22

system to any arbitrary excitation.   Consider the arbitrary excitation $f(t)$ of Fig. 22 to be applied to a system whose indicial and impulsive response are $g(t)$ and $h(t)$, respectively.   If the time is subdivided into increments of $\Delta\tau$, the curve $f(t)$ can be approximated by a series of incremental steps

$$\left[\frac{\Delta f(\tau)}{\Delta \tau}\right] \Delta \tau$$

Thus the response of the system to the first step $f(0)$ is

$$f(0)g(t)$$

and the response to the incremental step started at $t = \tau$ is

$$\left[\frac{\Delta f(\tau)}{\Delta \tau}\right] \Delta \tau \, g(t - \tau)$$

That is, the response to a unit step function applied at $t = \tau$ depends only on the elapsed time $(t - \tau)$ and would equal $g(t - \tau)$. The response at any time t is, then, the sum

$$x(t) = f(0)g(t) + \sum_{t=\Delta\tau}^{t} \frac{\Delta f(\tau)}{\Delta \tau} g(t - \tau) \, \Delta \tau \qquad (22.1)$$

If $\Delta \tau$ is allowed to approach zero, this sum has the limit

$$x(t) = f(0)g(t) + \int_0^t f'(\tau)g(t - \tau) \, d\tau \qquad (22.2)$$

which is referred to as the *superposition integral* or *Duhamel's integral*.

Equation (22.2) can be expressed in several different forms. Using the following substitution

$$u = g(t - \tau), \quad du = g'(t - \tau) \, d\tau$$
$$dv = f'(\tau) \, d\tau, \quad v = f(\tau)$$

and integrating by parts, we obtain the equation

$$x(t) = f(0)g(t) + f(\tau)g(t - \tau)\Big]_0^t + \int_0^t f(\tau)g'(t - \tau) \, d\tau$$
$$= \int_0^t f(\tau)g'(t - \tau) \, d\tau \qquad (22.3)$$

From the discussion in Section 15 it is evident that the impulsive response $h(t)$ is equal to the time rate of change of the indicial response $g(t)$. Thus by replacing $g'(t - \tau)$ by $h(t - \tau)$, we obtain the expression

$$x(t) = \int_0^t f(\tau)h(t - \tau) \, d\tau \qquad (22.4)$$
$$= f(t) * h(t)$$

This equation is referred to as the *convolution* or *Faltung* integral, and $f(t) * h(t)$ is an abbreviation which stands for the convolution of $f(t)$ and $h(t)$ as expressed by the given integral. Another form of Eq. (22.4) is

$$x(t) = \int_0^t f(t - \lambda)h(\lambda) \, d\lambda \tag{22.5}$$

which is obtained by letting $\lambda = t - \tau$.

These equations indicate that if the impulsive response $h(t)$ of a system is known, then the response to any arbitrary excitation $f(t)$ can be found. In cases where the integral is too complicated for analytical evaluation, it is always possible to resort to numerical or graphical integration.

23. Borel's Theorem. The convolution integral is linked with the operational method by Borel's theorem. To determine the equivalent operational form of Eq. (22.4), we can write the response transform $\bar{x}(s)$ to an arbitrary excitation $f(t)$:

$$\bar{x}(s) = \frac{\bar{f}(s)}{Z(s)} = \bar{f}(s)\bar{h}(s) \tag{23.1}$$

Comparing Eqs. (22.4) and (23.1), we obtain the relationship

$$x(t) = \mathcal{L}^{-1}\bar{f}(s)\bar{h}(s) = \int_0^t f(\tau)h(t - \tau) \, d\tau = f(t) * h(t) \tag{23.2}$$

Thus we have *Theorem* 12, which states that *the inverse transformation of the product of two subsidiary functions is equal to the convolution of their inverse.*

EXAMPLE 23.1: Find

$$\mathcal{L}^{-1} \frac{1}{(s + a)(s + b)}$$

by the convolution integral. We let

$$\bar{f}(s) = \frac{1}{s + a} \quad \text{and} \quad h(s) = \frac{1}{s + b}$$

Then $\qquad f(\tau) = e^{-a\tau} \quad \text{and} \quad h(t - \tau) = e^{-b(t-\tau)}$

Thus from Eq. (23.2) we have

$$x(t) = \int_0^t e^{-a\tau}e^{-b(t-\tau)} \, d\tau = e^{-bt} \int_0^t e^{-(a-b)\tau} \, d\tau$$

$$= \frac{e^{-bt}e^{-(a-b)\tau}}{-(a - b)} \bigg]_0^t = \frac{e^{-at} - e^{-bt}}{(b - a)}$$

EXAMPLE 23.2: Determine the response of the spring-mass system of Fig. 21 to an arbitrary force $f(t)$ with the initial conditions $x(0) = x'(0) = 0$.

The response of the system to a unit impulse is (see Example 21.1)

$$h(t) = \frac{1}{\sqrt{km}} \sin \sqrt{\frac{k}{m}}\, t$$

Thus the response to an arbitrary force $f(t)$, from Eq. (23.2), is

$$x(t) = \frac{1}{\sqrt{km}} \int_0^t f(\tau) \sin \sqrt{\frac{k}{m}}\, (t - \tau)\, d\tau$$

24. Steady-State Solution for Harmonic Excitation.   The steady-state response of a system to harmonic excitation can be readily determined from the subsidiary equation without carrying out the inverse transformation.   Writing the subsidiary equation in the form

$$\bar{y}(s) = \frac{\bar{F}(s)}{Z(s)} \tag{24.1}$$

where $\bar{F}(s)$ is the excitation and $Z(s)$ is the impedance transform, we can let $F(t) = e^{i\omega t}$ or

$$\bar{F}(s) = \frac{1}{s - i\omega} \tag{24.2}$$

Thus Eq. (24.1) becomes

$$\bar{y}(s) = \frac{1}{(s - i\omega)Z(s)} \tag{24.3}$$

The inverse of this equation is, then, equal to

$$y(t) = \frac{e^{i\omega t}}{Z(i\omega)} + \left\{ \frac{e^{st}}{(s - i\omega)Z'(s)} \right\}_{s=\text{roots of } Z(s)=0} \tag{24.4}$$

Since the second term of Eq. (24.4) leads only to transient terms, the steady-state solution becomes

$$y(t)_{ss} = \frac{F(t)}{Z(i\omega)} \tag{24.5}$$

where $F(t)$ is any harmonic excitation.

EXAMPLE 24.1: Determine the steady-state response of a spring-mass system with viscous damping when the impressed force is sinusoidal.

The differential equation of motion is

$$m\ddot{y} + c\dot{y} + ky = F_0 \sin \omega t$$

and
$$Z(i\omega) = m(i\omega)^2 + ci\omega + k$$
$$= \sqrt{(k - m\omega^2)^2 + (c\omega)^2}\, e^{i\varphi}$$
$$\varphi = \tan^{-1} \frac{c\omega}{k - m\omega^2}$$

Thus from Eq. (24.5)

$$y(t)_{ss} = \frac{F_0\, e^{-i\varphi} \sin \omega t}{\sqrt{(k - m\omega^2)^2 + (c\omega)^2}} = \frac{F_0 \sin (\omega t - \varphi)}{\sqrt{(k - m\omega^2)^2 + (c\omega)^2}}$$

Problems

61. Determine the indicial admittance of the massless spring of stiffness k lb/in. in parallel with a dashpot c lb-sec/in. shown in Fig. 23.

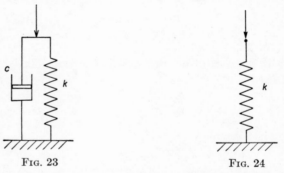

FIG. 23   FIG. 24

62. If a constant force $F_0 \mathcal{U}(t)$ is applied to a massless spring of Fig. 24, determine the velocity and displacement of the end as a function of time.

63. Repeat Prob. 62 if an impulsive force $I_0 \mathcal{U}'(t)$ is applied.

64. If an impulse I_0 lb-sec is applied to the system of Fig. 23, show that the velocity and displacement of the end are given by

$$\dot{x}(t) = \frac{I_0}{c} \left\{ \mathcal{U}'(t) - \frac{k}{c} e^{-\frac{k}{c}t} \right\}$$

$$x(t) = \frac{I_0}{c} e^{-\frac{k}{c}t}$$

Interpret these solutions physically.

65. Derive Eq. (22.4) by subdividing $f(t)$ into impulsive components.

66. The indicial response of a system is given as $g(t) = (1 - e^{-kt})$. Determine the response of the system to a force $\sin (pt + \varphi)$.

67. Show that

$$\mathcal{L}^{-1} \left(\frac{s - \alpha}{s + \alpha} \right) = \mathcal{L}^{-1} \left\{ 1 - \frac{2\alpha}{s + \alpha} \right\} = \mathcal{U}'(t) - 2\alpha \, e^{-\alpha t}$$

68. Prove that

$$\mathcal{L}^{-1} \frac{1}{s} = \mathcal{U}'(t) * \mathcal{U}(t) = \int_0^t \mathcal{U}'(\tau) \mathcal{U}(t - \tau) \, d\tau = 1$$

This problem should be visualized in terms of Fig. 25.

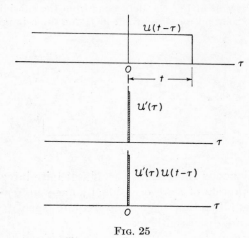

Fig. 25

69. Using the procedure of Chapter 1, we can show that

$$\mathcal{L}^{-1} \frac{1}{s} \left(\frac{s - \alpha}{s + \alpha} \right) = -1 + 2 \, e^{-\alpha t}$$

By Borel's theorem, show that the same result is obtained from

$$\mathcal{L}^{-1} \frac{1}{s} \left(\frac{s - \alpha}{s + \alpha} \right) = \mathcal{U}(t) * [\mathcal{U}'(t) - 2\alpha \, e^{-\alpha t}]$$

70. Using the result given in Prob. 69, show by Borel's theorem that

$$\mathcal{L}^{-1}\frac{1}{s^2}\left(\frac{s-\alpha}{s+\alpha}\right) = \frac{2}{\alpha} - t - \frac{2}{\alpha}e^{-\alpha t}$$

$$\mathcal{L}^{-1}\frac{1}{s^2}\left(\frac{s-\alpha}{s+\alpha}\right)^2 = -\frac{4}{\alpha} + t + 4\left(t - \frac{1}{\alpha}\right)e^{-\alpha t}$$

71. Show that the sum of two conjugate complex quantities is equal to twice the real component of either term. Show that the sum of the first two terms of Prob. 41 is equal to

$$2\Re\left[\frac{A(i\omega)\,e^{i\omega t}}{2i\omega\,B_1(i\omega)}\right]$$

where $\Re$ stands for the real part of the quantity.

72. For the circuit of Fig. 26, determine from the subsidiary equation the steady-state solution for the current in R due to an impressed voltage of $E \sin \omega t$.

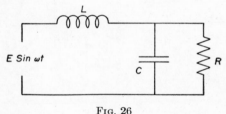

Fig. 26

25. Miscellaneous Integrals.

Certain definite integrals involving fractional powers of t are occasionally encountered in physical problems. Such functions generally require special techniques, some of which are discussed here.

The Gamma Function. If $f(t) = t^n$, its transform

$$\mathcal{L}t^n = \int_0^\infty e^{-st}t^n \, dt \qquad (25.1)$$

can be shown to exist for $n > -1$.

When a new variable $x = st$ is introduced, Eq. 25.1 becomes

$$\mathcal{L}t^n = \frac{1}{s^{n+1}}\int_0^\infty e^{-x}x^n \, dx \qquad (25.2)$$

The above integral is a tabulated function known as the *Gamma*

function $\Gamma(n + 1)$ which is continuous for $n > -1$. Thus

$$\mathcal{L}t^n = \frac{\Gamma(n + 1)}{s^{n+1}} \qquad (n > -1) \quad (25.3)$$

For integer values of n, $\Gamma(n + 1) = n!$, and Eq. (25.3) reduces to the known form

$$\mathcal{L}t^n = \frac{n!}{s^{n+1}} \qquad (n \text{ an integer}) \quad (25.4)$$

Of special interest is the case where $n = -\frac{1}{2}$. Eq. (25.3) then becomes

$$\left.\begin{aligned} \mathcal{L}t^{-\frac{1}{2}} &= \frac{\Gamma(\frac{1}{2})}{s^{\frac{1}{2}}} = \sqrt{\frac{\pi}{s}} \\ \mathcal{L}^{-1} s^{-\frac{1}{2}} &= \frac{1}{\sqrt{\pi t}} \end{aligned}\right\} \quad (25.5)$$

or

The transforms of $t^{\frac{1}{2}}$, $t^{\frac{3}{2}}$, . . . , can be readily obtained from this equation by the application of Theorem 8.

The Error Function. The error function is another tabulated function. It is defined by the equation

$$\operatorname{erf}(x) = \frac{2}{\sqrt{\pi}} \int_0^x e^{-\lambda^2}\, d\lambda \quad (25.6)$$

We shall now consider some transforms resulting in the error function.

First we shall investigate the inverse transform

$$\mathcal{L}^{-1} \frac{1}{\sqrt{s}\,(s - 1)} \quad (25.7)$$

From Eq. (25.5), $\mathcal{L}^{-1} \dfrac{1}{\sqrt{s}} = \dfrac{1}{\sqrt{\pi t}}$

Also $\mathcal{L}^{-1} \dfrac{1}{s - 1} = e^t$

Thus by the use of the convolution integral,

$$\mathcal{L}^{-1} \frac{1}{\sqrt{s}\,(s - 1)} = \int_0^t \frac{e^{(t-\tau)}}{\sqrt{\pi \tau}}\, d\tau = \frac{e^t}{\sqrt{\pi}} \int_0^t \frac{e^{-\tau}}{\sqrt{\tau}}\, d\tau \quad (25.8)$$

If a new variable $\lambda = \sqrt{\tau}$ is introduced, the above integral becomes

$$\mathcal{L}^{-1} \frac{1}{\sqrt{s}\,(s - 1)} = \frac{2 e^t}{\sqrt{\pi}} \int_0^{\sqrt{t}} e^{-\lambda^2}\, d\lambda = e^t \operatorname{erf}(\sqrt{t}) \quad (25.9)$$

Using the first shifting theorem, we obtain another transform pair:

$$\mathcal{L}^{-1} \frac{1}{s\sqrt{s+1}} = \text{erf}\,(\sqrt{t}) = \frac{2}{\sqrt{\pi}} \int_0^{\sqrt{t}} e^{-\lambda^2}\, d\lambda \qquad (25.10)$$

Consider next the function

$$f(t) = \frac{e^{-\frac{a^2}{4t}}}{\sqrt{\pi t}} \qquad (25.11)$$

To evaluate its transform,

$$\bar{f}(s) = \int_0^{\infty} e^{-st} \frac{e^{-\frac{a^2}{4t}}}{\sqrt{\pi t}}\, dt \qquad (25.12)$$

let $\sqrt{t} = \lambda$ and write

$$\bar{f}(s) = \frac{2}{\sqrt{\pi}} \int_0^{\infty} e^{-s\left(\lambda^2 + \frac{a^2}{4s\lambda^2}\right)}\, d\lambda \qquad (25.13)$$

Since $$s\left(\lambda^2 + \frac{a^2}{4s\lambda^2}\right) = s\left(\lambda - \frac{a}{2\sqrt{s}\,\lambda}\right)^2 + a\sqrt{s}$$

$$\bar{f}(s) = \frac{2\,e^{-a\sqrt{s}}}{\sqrt{\pi}} \int_0^{\infty} e^{-s\left(\lambda - \frac{a}{2\sqrt{s}\,\lambda}\right)^2}\, d\lambda$$

$$= \frac{2\,e^{-a\sqrt{s}}}{\sqrt{\pi}} \int_0^{\infty} e^{-s\left(\lambda - \frac{b}{\lambda}\right)^2}\, d\lambda \qquad (25.14)$$

where $b = a/2\sqrt{s}$. We next make the substitution

$$\tau = \frac{b}{\lambda}, \quad d\lambda = -\frac{b}{\tau^2}\, d\tau$$

and write for the above integral

$$\int_0^{\infty} e^{-s\left(\lambda - \frac{b}{\lambda}\right)^2}\, d\lambda = -\int_{\infty}^{0} \frac{b}{\tau^2} e^{-s\left(\frac{b}{\tau} - \tau\right)^2}\, d\tau = \int_0^{\infty} \frac{b}{\tau^2} e^{-s\left(\tau - \frac{b}{\tau}\right)^2}\, d\tau$$
$$(25.15)$$

Adding the integral on the left to each side, we obtain

$$2\int_0^{\infty} e^{-s\left(\lambda - \frac{b}{\lambda}\right)^2}\, d\lambda = \int_0^{\infty}\left(1 + \frac{b}{\tau^2}\right) e^{-s\left(\tau - \frac{b}{\tau}\right)^2}\, d\tau \qquad (25.16)$$

If we let $$x = \sqrt{s}\left(\tau - \frac{b}{\tau}\right), \quad dx = \sqrt{s}\left(1 + \frac{b}{\tau^2}\right) d\tau$$

Eq. (25.16) becomes

$$2 \int_0^\infty e^{-s\left(\lambda - \frac{b}{\lambda}\right)^2} d\lambda = \frac{1}{\sqrt{s}} \int_{-\infty}^\infty e^{-x^2} dx = \frac{2}{\sqrt{s}} \int_0^\infty e^{-x^2} dx = \sqrt{\frac{\pi}{s}}$$

(25.17)

Substituting back into Eq. (25.14), we obtain the final expression*

$$\bar{f}(s) = \frac{e^{-a\sqrt{s}}}{\sqrt{s}} = \mathcal{L} \frac{e^{-\frac{a^2}{4t}}}{\sqrt{\pi t}}$$

(25.18)

By making use of some of the theorems in this chapter, we can obtain other transform pairs. From Theorem 9,

$$\mathcal{L} \frac{f(t)}{t} = \int_s^\infty \bar{f}(s) \, ds$$

If we let

$$f(t) = \frac{e^{-\frac{a^2}{4t}}}{\sqrt{\pi t}}$$

then

$$\bar{f}(s) = \frac{e^{-a\sqrt{s}}}{\sqrt{s}}$$

$$\int_s^\infty \bar{f}(s) \, ds = \int_s^\infty e^{-a\sqrt{s}} s^{-\frac{1}{2}} \, ds = -\frac{2}{a} \int_s^\infty d(e^{-a\sqrt{s}})$$

$$= -\frac{2}{a} e^{-a\sqrt{s}} \Big]_s^\infty = \frac{2}{a} e^{-a\sqrt{s}}$$

Therefore

$$\mathcal{L} \frac{e^{-\frac{a^2}{4t}}}{\sqrt{\pi t^3}} = \frac{2}{a} e^{-a\sqrt{s}}$$

(25.19)

We next make use of Theorem 7, which can be written as

$$\mathcal{L}^{-1} \frac{\bar{f}(s)}{s} = \int_0^t f(t) \, dt$$

If Eq. (25.18) is substituted into the above formula,

$$\mathcal{L}^{-1} \frac{e^{-a\sqrt{s}}}{s} = \frac{a}{2\sqrt{\pi}} \int_0^t e^{-\frac{a^2}{4t}} t^{-\frac{3}{2}} \, dt$$

(25.20)

* The procedure used here is similar to that used by Churchill (Ref. 12, Bibliography), page 58, for the evaluation of the transform of $t^{-\frac{3}{2}} e^{\frac{k^2}{4t}}$.

If we let $\lambda = a/2 \sqrt{t}$, the integral on the right becomes

$$\frac{2}{\sqrt{\pi}} \int_{\frac{a}{2\sqrt{t}}}^{\infty} e^{-\lambda^2} d\lambda = \frac{2}{\sqrt{\pi}} \int_{0}^{\infty} e^{-\lambda^2} d\lambda - \frac{2}{\sqrt{\pi}} \int_{0}^{\frac{a}{2\sqrt{t}}} e^{-\lambda^2} d\lambda$$

Therefore $\qquad \mathcal{L}^{-1} \dfrac{e^{-a\sqrt{s}}}{s} = 1 - \text{erf}\left(\dfrac{a}{2\sqrt{t}}\right)$ $\qquad$ (25.21)

It should be pointed out that the inverse transform of functions containing $e^{-a\sqrt{s}}$ is sometimes obtained by expanding the exponential in the series form and operating on each term separately. This procedure, however, requires the use of the relation

$$\mathcal{L}^{-1} \frac{1}{s^{n+1}} = \frac{t^n}{\Gamma(n + 1)}$$

for half integers with $n < -1$. As has been discussed under The Gamma Function, the above equation is strictly limited for $n > -1$, and its questionable use for $n < -1$ must be justified.*

Problems

73. Applying Theorem 8 to Eq. (25.5), determine the transform of $t^{\frac{1}{2}}$ and $t^{\frac{3}{2}}$.

74. In Eq. (25.2) let $n = -\frac{1}{2}$ and $x = \lambda^2$, and show that

$$\mathcal{L}t^{-\frac{1}{2}} = \frac{2}{s^{\frac{1}{2}}} \int_{0}^{\infty} e^{-\lambda^2} d\lambda$$

Comparing this result with Eq. (25.5), show that

$$2 \int_{0}^{\infty} e^{-\lambda^2} d\lambda = \sqrt{\pi}$$

75. For integer values of n we have $\Gamma(n + 1) = n!$ Show that $\Gamma(1) = 0! = 1$. Note that $(n - 1)! = n!/n$.

76. Prove that $\int_{0}^{\infty} e^{-\lambda^2} d\lambda = \sqrt{\pi}/2$. Let

$$I = \int_{0}^{a} e^{-x^2} dx = \int_{0}^{a} e^{-v^2} dy$$

and express $\qquad I^2 = \int_{0}^{a} \int_{0}^{a} e^{-(x^2+v^2)} dx \, dy$

* See Goldman (Ref. 14, Bibliography), page 331.

in polar coordinates.   The value of I^2 must then lie between the integrated values over the circular quadrants of radius a and $a\sqrt{2}$.   By letting $a \to \infty$, the desired result is obtained.

77. Show that

$$\mathcal{L}^{-1}\frac{1}{\sqrt{s}+1} = \frac{1}{\sqrt{\pi t}} - e^t(1 + \operatorname{erf}\sqrt{t})$$

CHAPTER 3

Dynamical Applications

In many cases, mechanical systems can be idealized in terms of linear springs, masses, and dashpots. Much information can be obtained by studying the behavior of such simplified systems subjected to various dynamical conditions. Such problems involve only ordinary differential equations with constant coefficients for which the subsidiary equations are rational algebraic functions.

26. Automatic Control Mechanisms. Regulation of pressures, flow, speed, and similar characteristics are frequently controlled automatically. In this section we shall describe two automatic regulatory devices and investigate their dynamical behavior due to a sudden change in the load.

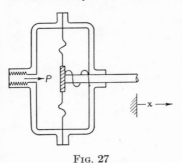

(a) Figure 27 shows the essential parts of a pressure-operated control valve. Assuming a sudden increase in the pressure in the form of a unit step function, the differential equation of motion of the valve becomes

Fig. 27

$$m\ddot{x} + c\dot{x} + kx = P\mathfrak{U}(t) \quad (26.1)$$

where m is the effective mass of the moving parts, c the damping constant (assumed to be viscous), and k the spring stiffness. For convenience, we shall rewrite this equation thus:

$$\ddot{x} + 2\alpha\omega\dot{x} + \omega^2 x = \frac{P}{m}\mathfrak{U}(t) \quad (26.2)$$

where
$$\omega = \sqrt{\frac{k}{m}} \quad \text{and} \quad \alpha = \frac{c}{2m\omega}$$

With the system initially at rest, the subsidiary equation is

$$\bar{x}(s) = \frac{P}{ms(s^2 + 2\alpha\omega s + \omega^2)} = \frac{P}{ms(s - s_1)(s - s_2)} \quad (26.3)$$

48

where the zeros of the denominator are

$$s_0 = 0$$
$$s_{1,2} = \omega(-\alpha \pm i\sqrt{1 - \alpha^2}) = \omega(-\alpha \pm i\beta)$$

The inverse transformation, from Eq. (8.5), is then

$$x(t) = \frac{P}{m}\left[\frac{1}{s_1 s_2} + \frac{e^{s_1 t}}{s_1(s_1 - s_2)} + \frac{e^{s_2 t}}{s_2(s_2 - s_1)}\right]$$
$$= \frac{P}{m}\left[\frac{1}{s_1 s_2} + \frac{1}{(s_1 - s_2)}\left(\frac{e^{s_1 t}}{s_1} - \frac{e^{s_2 t}}{s_2}\right)\right] \tag{26.4}$$

Since s_1 and s_2 are conjugate complex quantities, the last part of this equation, representing the difference of conjugate quantities,

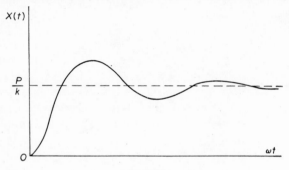

FIG. 28

is equal to twice the imaginary part of the first term, **or**

$$x(t) = \frac{P}{m}\left[\frac{1}{s_1 s_2} + \frac{1}{(s_1 - s_2)}\, 2\mathcal{I}\left(\frac{e^{s_1 t}}{s_1}\right)\right]$$
$$= \frac{P}{m}\left\{\frac{1}{\omega^2(\alpha^2 + \beta^2)} + \frac{1}{i\omega\beta}\,\mathcal{I}\left[\frac{(-\alpha - i\beta)\,e^{(-\alpha+i\beta)\omega t}}{\omega(\alpha^2 + \beta^2)}\right]\right\}$$
$$= \frac{P}{\omega^2 m}\left[1 - \frac{e^{-\alpha\omega t}}{i\beta}\,i(\beta\cos\beta\omega t + \alpha\sin\beta\omega t)\right]$$
$$\left.\begin{array}{c} = \frac{P}{k}\left\{1 - \frac{e^{-\alpha\omega t}}{\sqrt{1 - \alpha^2}}\cos(\omega t\sqrt{1 - \alpha^2} - \varphi)\right\} \\[2mm] \varphi = \tan^{-1}\frac{\alpha}{\sqrt{1 - \alpha^2}} \end{array}\right\} \tag{26.5}$$

A typical plot of this equation is shown in Fig. 28, which indicates that the motion is a damped oscillation about its final position.

(b) Figure 29 shows a hydraulic device sometimes used in automatic control mechanisms.   The cylinder is movable in the horizontal direction and is completely filled with oil.   The valve v
restricts the passage of the fluid.   If the piston is given a sudden
displacement, the cylinder must follow, since the valve cannot allow
any appreciable flow in an infinitesimal time.   However, since the
oil flows through this valve, the spring under compression will
gradually allow the cylinder to return to its original position, the
rate of this motion being determined by the valve opening.

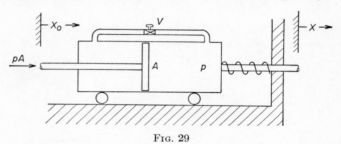

Fig. 29

Assuming that the piston is suddenly displaced an amount x_0
and held in this position, the differential equation of motion of the
cylinder becomes

$$m\ddot{x} = -kx + pA \qquad (26.6)$$

with the initial conditions

$$x(0) = x_0, \quad \dot{x}(0) = 0 \qquad (26.7)$$

In this equation p is the fluid pressure to the right of the piston
(pressure in the left chamber is taken to be zero), and A the piston
area.

The motion of the cylinder from its initial position x_0 is due to
flow through the valve V, and we have the equations

$$\text{Volume flowing through } V = A(x_0 - x)$$

$$\text{Rate of flow through } V = -A\dot{x}$$

Since this rate of flow is proportional to the pressure, we can write

$$cp = -A\dot{x} \qquad (26.8)$$

where c is a constant of proportionality.   Substituting for p in the differential equation gives

$$\ddot{x} + \left(\frac{A^2}{cm}\right)\dot{x} + \frac{k}{m}x = 0 \qquad (26.9)$$

If we let
$$\omega = \sqrt{\frac{k}{m}}, \quad \alpha = \frac{1}{2\omega}\left(\frac{A^2}{cm}\right)$$

Eq. (26.9) can be rewritten as

$$\ddot{x} + 2\alpha\omega\dot{x} + \omega^2 x = 0 \qquad (26.10)$$

With the initial conditions as specified by Eq. (26.7), the subsidiary equation becomes

$$s^2\bar{x}(s) - sx_0 + 2\alpha\omega[s\bar{x}(s) - x_0] + \omega^2\bar{x}(s) = 0$$

$$\bar{x}(s) = \frac{(s + 2\alpha\omega)x_0}{s^2 + 2\alpha\omega s + \omega^2} = \frac{(s + 2\alpha\omega)x_0}{(s - s_1)(s - s_2)} \qquad (26.11)$$

The zeros of the denominator s_1 and s_2 are

$$s_{1,2} = \omega(-\alpha \pm \sqrt{\alpha^2 - 1})$$

where α is assumed to be greater than 1, to correspond to the case

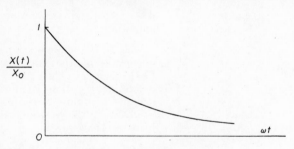

Fig. 30

of aperiodic motion.   Thus, from Eq. (8.5), we can write

$$\frac{x(t)}{x_0} = \frac{(s_1 + 2\alpha\omega)\,e^{s_1 t}}{s_1 - s_2} + \frac{(s_2 + 2\alpha\omega)\,e^{s_2 t}}{s_2 - s_1}$$

$$= \frac{(s_1 + 2\alpha\omega)\,e^{s_1 t} - (s_2 + 2\alpha\omega)\,e^{s_2 t}}{s_1 - s_2}$$

$$= \frac{1}{2\sqrt{\alpha^2 - 1}}\,[(\alpha + \sqrt{\alpha^2 - 1})\,e^{(-\alpha + \sqrt{\alpha^2 - 1})\omega t}$$

$$- (\alpha - \sqrt{\alpha^2 - 1})\,e^{(-\alpha - \sqrt{\alpha^2 - 1})\omega t}] \qquad (26.12)$$

The final equation plotted in Fig. 30 indicates that the motion of the cylinder is that of exponential decay with α determining its rate.

Problems

78. If a rectangular pressure pulse of magnitude P and time duration t_1 is applied to the system of Fig. 27, determine the motion of the valve. *Hint:* To the solution given in Section 26, superimpose the solution for a negative pressure started at t_1.

79. What additional term is introduced if the valve of Fig. 27 is moving with a velocity v_0 at the time a sudden pressure increase in the form of a step function is applied?

80. If an impulse of magnitude I_0 lb-sec is applied to a spring-mass system with viscous damping, determine its motion for the initial conditions $x(0) = \dot{x}(0) = 0$.

81. A viscously damped spring-mass system of natural frequency ω is excited by a harmonic force $F_0 \sin \omega t$. If the system starts from rest, determine the equation of motion. Obtain an equation for the time required for the amplitude to build up to x_0. From the subsidiary equation, determine the maximum steady state amplitude.

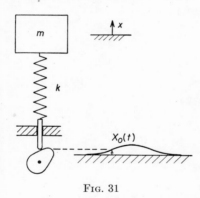

Fig. 31

82. If the undamped natural frequency ω of the automatic control mechanism of Fig. 29 is 20 cpm, determine the time required for the cylinder to return to the position $x(t) = 0.20x_0$ if the by-pass valve is adjusted so that $\alpha = 4$.

27. Prescribed Motion of Support. Figure 31 shows a spring-mass system the lower end of which undergoes a motion $x_0(t)$ prescribed by the cam. The differential equation of motion of m is

$$m\ddot{x} = k[x_0(t) - x] \qquad (27.1)$$

or
$$\ddot{x} + \omega^2 x = \omega^2 x_0(t)$$

$$\omega^2 = \frac{k}{m}$$

If the system is started from rest, the subsidiary equation for the displacement of m is

$$\bar{x}(s) = \frac{\omega^2 \bar{x}_0(s)}{s^2 + \omega^2} \tag{27.2}$$

from which $x(t)$ can be found when $x_0(t)$ is specified.

Frequently the quantity of interest is the force exerted on m by the spring, in which case we are concerned with the relative motion

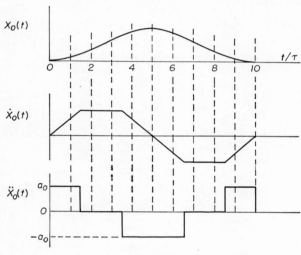

Fig. 32

$z = x_0(t) - x$ of the ends of the spring. From Eq. (27.1), we can write

$$F = kz = m\ddot{x}$$

from which the subsidiary equation becomes

$$\bar{F}(s) = k\bar{z}(s) = ms^2\bar{x}(s) = \frac{m\omega^2 s^2 \bar{x}_0(s)}{s^2 + \omega^2} \tag{27.3}$$

EXAMPLE 27.1: Determine the force on the mass m when the cam motion is described by Fig. 32 and the natural period of the spring-mass system is τ.

We note from Eq. (27.3) that the numerator contains the term $s^2\bar{x}_0(x)$, which is the transform of the acceleration of the lower end of the spring. Also, the acceleration shown in Fig. 32 can be obtained by properly superimposing step functions of height a, starting at $t = 0, 1.5\tau, 3.5\tau, \ldots$ Thus we need only the solution for a step function $s^2\bar{x}_0(s) = a_0/s$, or the inversion of the equation

$$\bar{F}(s) = \frac{m\omega^2 a_0}{s(s^2 + \omega^2)} \tag{27.4}$$

which is
$$F(t) = ma_0(1 - \cos \omega t) \tag{27.5}$$

Equation (27.5) represents a harmonic oscillation between the values 0 and $2ma_0$. By superimposing such curves, starting it in

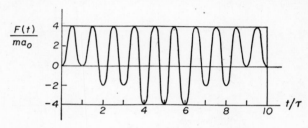

Fig. 33

the negative direction at 1.5τ, 3.5τ, and again in the positive direction at 6.5τ, and so on, we obtain the resulting force variation shown by the curve of Fig. 33.

Problems

83. If the cam of Fig. 31 has the motion shown in Fig. 34, determine the spring force.

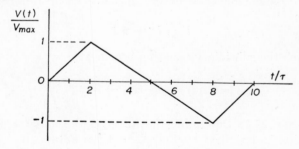

Fig. 34

84. Figure 35 shows a simplified representation of a vehicle traveling with velocity v and running over a sinusoidal bump. Determine the vertical motion of m as a function of v, and its natural frequency.

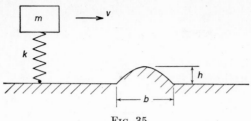

FIG. 35

85. A spring-mass system rests on a platform A as shown in Fig. 36. If the platform is started down with an acceleration ng, where $n > 1$, determine the equation of motion of the mass m and show that the platform will leave the ends of the spring when $\cos \omega t = 1 - 1/n$.

28. Dynamic Load Factor Due to Impulse.*

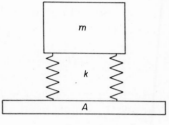

FIG. 36

If a force of constant magnitude F_0 is applied to the system of Fig. 37 for a time t_1, common sense tells us that the amplitude or acceleration developed by m will increase with t_1. We shall now define the dynamic load factor as the ratio of the maximum dynamic spring force to the spring force developed under a static force F_0 and shall study how this quantity

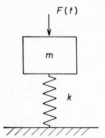

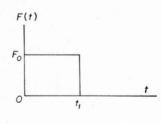

FIG. 37

depends on t_1/τ, where $\tau = 2\pi \sqrt{m/k}$ is the natural period of the spring-mass system.

Measuring displacement x from the equilibrium position, we

* J. M. Frankland, "Effect of Impact on Simple Elastic Structures," *Proc. of Society for Experimental Stress Analysis*, Vol. 6, No. 2, pages 7–27.

find that the differential equation of motion is

$$m\ddot{x} = -kx + F_0[\mathfrak{U}(t) - \mathfrak{U}(t - t_1)] \tag{28.1}$$

With the system started from rest in the equilibrium position, the subsidiary equation becomes

$$\bar{x}(s) = \frac{F_0}{m} \frac{(1 - e^{-st_1})}{s(s^2 + \omega^2)} \qquad \left(\omega^2 = \frac{k}{m}\right) \tag{28.2}$$

From Theorem 7, we have

$$\mathcal{L}^{-1} \frac{\omega}{s(s^2 + \omega^2)} = \int_0^t \sin \omega t \, dt = \frac{1}{\omega}(1 - \cos \omega t) \tag{28.3}$$

The exponential e^{-st_1} only shifts the above function along the t axis by t_1. Thus

$$x(t) = \frac{F_0}{m\omega^2} \{(1 - \cos \omega t) - [1 - \cos \omega(t - t_1)]\mathfrak{U}(t - t_1)\} \tag{28.4}$$

Since the function $\mathfrak{U}(t - t_1)$ is zero for $t < t_1$ and 1 for $t > t_1$, Eq. (28.4) is interpreted as

$$x(t) = \frac{F_0}{m\omega^2}(1 - \cos \omega t) \qquad (0 \le t \le t_1) \tag{28.5}$$

$$= \frac{F_0}{m\omega^2}[\cos \omega t - \cos \omega(t - t_1)]$$

$$= \frac{2F_0}{m\omega^2} \sin \frac{\omega t_1}{2} \sin \omega \left(t - \frac{t_1}{2}\right) \quad (t \ge t_1) \tag{28.6}$$

Expressed in nondimensional form, these equations can be written as

$$\frac{x(t)}{x_{\text{st}}} = \left(1 - \cos 2\pi \frac{t}{\tau}\right) \qquad (0 \le t \le t_1) \tag{28.7}$$

$$= 2 \sin \pi \frac{t_1}{\tau} \sin 2\pi \left(\frac{t}{\tau} - \frac{t_1}{2\tau}\right) \quad (t \ge t_1) \tag{28.8}$$

These equations indicate that $x(t)/x_{\text{st}}$ is a function only of the ratio t_1/τ. If $t_1 \ge \tau/2$, Eq. (28.7) shows that an amplitude ratio of 2 will be reached. If $t_1 < \tau/2$, the amplitude ratio from Eq. (28.8) is $2 \sin \pi t_1/\tau$. Since the force and acceleration are both proportional to the amplitude in this case, the dynamic load factor then becomes

$$2 \quad \text{for} \quad \frac{t_1}{\tau} \geq \frac{1}{2}$$

$$2 \sin \frac{\pi t_1}{\tau} \quad \text{for} \quad \frac{t_1}{\tau} < \frac{1}{2}$$

Curves for $x(t)/x_{\text{st}}$ and the dynamic load factor are plotted in Figs. 38 and 39.   Thus, for a short rectangular pulse $t_1/\tau \leq \frac{1}{2}$, the

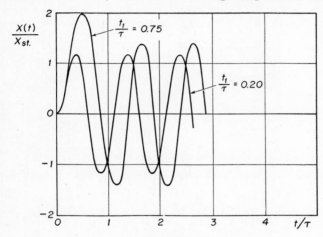

Fig. 38

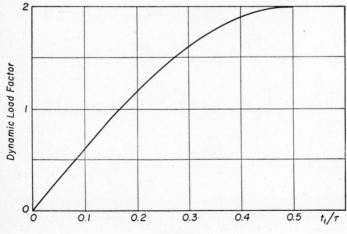

Fig. 39

dynamic load factor is less than 2, and for a long rectangular pulse $t_1/\tau \geq \frac{1}{2}$ it is always 2.

Problems

86. Determine the motion and dynamic load factor of a spring-mass system subjected to a rectangular force pulse of duration t_1 if (a) $t_1/\tau = \frac{1}{5}$, (b) $t_1/\tau = \frac{1}{10}$, (c) $t_1/\tau = 1.25$, (d) $t_1/\tau = 1.5$.

87. Determine the response and dynamic load factor for a spring-mass system subjected to a triangular force pulse of maximum value F_0 and time duration t_1.

The force pulse is given as

$$F(t) = 2F_0 \frac{t}{t_1} \qquad \text{for} \quad 0 \leq t \leq 0.5t_1$$
$$= 2F_0 \left(1 - \frac{t}{t_1}\right) \quad \text{for} \quad 0.5t_1 \leq t \leq t_1$$
$$= 0 \qquad \text{for} \quad t \geq t_1$$

Write a separate solution for each of these intervals.

88. Repeat Prob. 87 for a sinusoidal pulse of height F_0 and base t_1.

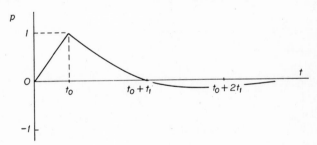

FIG. 40

89. Figure 40 shows a typical pressure disturbance due to a gun blast, where

$$p = \frac{t}{t_0} \qquad\qquad\qquad (t \leq t_0)$$
$$= e^{-\left(\frac{t-t_0}{t_1}\right)} \left[1 - \frac{t - t_0}{t_1}\right] \qquad (t \geq t_0)$$

(a) Taking $t_0 = 0$ for a simplified analysis, determine the response and the dynamic load factor of a spring-mass system subjected to the blast. Plot the dynamic load factor as a function of t_1/τ, where τ is the natural period of the spring-mass system.

(b) Repeat with $t_0 \neq 0$ and show that the dynamic load factor is a function of t_0/τ and t_1/t_0.

90. Determine the response of an undamped spring-mass system to the force shown in Fig. 41. Determine the dynamic load factor and plot it as a function of t_1/τ, where τ is the natural period of the system.

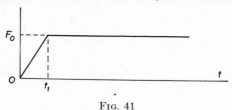

FIG. 41

29. Impact of Falling Bodies (Drop Tests). The question of how far a body can be dropped without incurring damage is of frequent interest. Such considerations are of paramount importance in the landing of airplanes or the cushioning of packaged articles.* In this section we shall discuss some of the elementary aspects of this problem by idealizing the mechanical system in terms of linear spring-mass components with viscous damping.

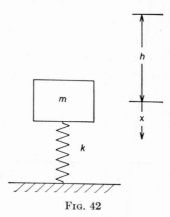

FIG. 42

(a) *Undamped System.* Consider the system of Fig. 42 dropped through a height h. If x is measured from the position of m at the instant $t = 0$ when the spring first contacts the floor, the differential equation of motion for m applicable as long as the spring remains in contact with the floor is

$$m\ddot{x} + kx = mg \qquad (29.1)$$

By using the initial conditions

$$\left. \begin{array}{l} x(0) = 0 \\ \dot{x}(0) = \sqrt{2gh} \end{array} \right\} \qquad (29.2)$$

* An extensive treatment of this problem, with emphasis on nonlinear cushioning, is given in R. D. Mindlin, "Dynamics of Package Cushioning," *Bell System Tech. Jour.*, **24**, 3–4 (July–October 1945), pages 353–461. The treatment does not make use of Laplace transformation, however.

we can write the subsidiary equation as

$$\bar{x}(s) = \frac{\sqrt{2gh}}{s^2 + \omega^2} + \frac{g}{s(s^2 + \omega^2)} \tag{29.3}$$

where $\omega = \sqrt{k/m}$. From the inverse transformation of $\bar{x}(s)$, the displacement equation becomes

$$\begin{aligned} x(t) &= \frac{\sqrt{2gh}}{\omega} \sin \omega t - \frac{g}{\omega^2} \cos \omega t + \frac{g}{\omega^2} \\ &= \sqrt{\frac{2gh}{\omega^2} + \left(\frac{g}{\omega^2}\right)^2} \left[\frac{\sqrt{2gh/\omega^2} \sin \omega t}{\sqrt{2gh/\omega^2 + (g/\omega^2)^2}} - \frac{g/\omega^2 \cos \omega t}{\sqrt{2gh/\omega^2 + (g/\omega^2)^2}} \right] \\ &\qquad + \frac{g}{\omega^2} \end{aligned}$$

$$\left. \begin{aligned} &= \sqrt{\frac{2gh}{\omega^2} + \left(\frac{g}{\omega^2}\right)^2} \sin (\omega t - \varphi) + \frac{g}{\omega^2} \\ &\varphi = \tan^{-1} \frac{g}{\omega \sqrt{2gh}} \end{aligned} \right\} \tag{29.4}$$

We note here that $g/\omega^2 = W/k$ is the statical deflection and $\sqrt{2gh/\omega^2}$ is the dynamical deflection due to h. Frequently the statical deflection is small compared to the dynamical deflection, and further simplification of the equations is possible.

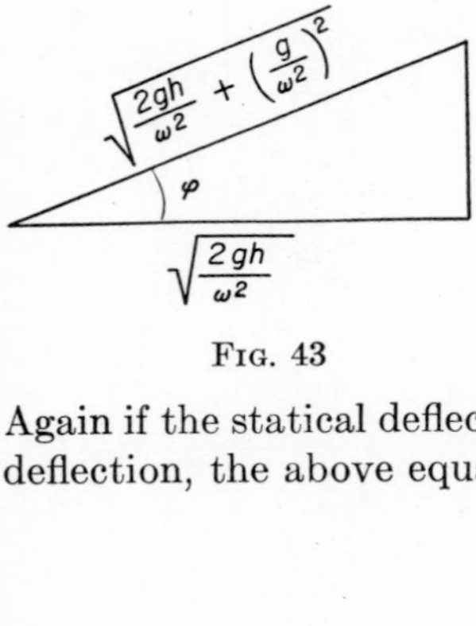

FIG. 43

To determine when the lower end of the spring will leave the floor, we let $x(t) = 0$ and obtain the equation

$$\sin (\omega t - \varphi) = \frac{-g/\omega^2}{\sqrt{2gh/\omega^2 + (g/\omega^2)^2}} \tag{29.5}$$

Again if the statical deflection is small compared with the dynamical deflection, the above equation reduces to

$$\begin{aligned} \sin \omega t &= 0 \\ t &= \frac{\pi}{\omega} \end{aligned} \tag{29.6}$$

From design considerations, we are more interested in the force or acceleration, which can be obtained by differentiating Eq. (29.4):

$$\ddot{x}(t) = -\sqrt{2gh\omega^2 + g^2} \sin (\omega t - \varphi) \tag{29.7}$$

Substituting for φ, we find that the acceleration starts with the value g as expected and builds up sinusoidally to a maximum value of $g - \sqrt{2gh\omega^2 + g^2}$, as shown in Fig. 44. The curve is reduced to nondimensional form $\ddot{x}(t)/g$. It is evident that the maximum

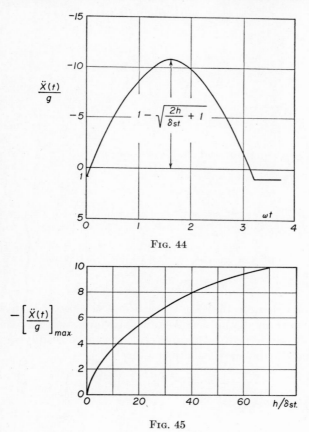

FIG. 44

FIG. 45

acceleration in terms of gravity depends only on the ratio of the distance dropped to the statical deflection and is equal to

$$\left[\frac{\ddot{x}(t)}{g}\right]_{\max} = 1 - \sqrt{\frac{2h}{\delta_{\text{st}}} + 1} \tag{29.8}$$

A plot of this equation is shown in Fig. 45.

(b) *Effect of Damping.*   Assuming viscous damping (see Fig. 46), the differential equation after contact of the lower end with the floor is

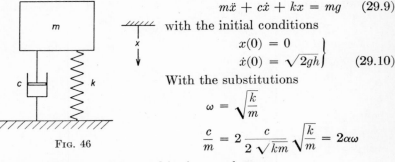

$$m\ddot{x} + c\dot{x} + kx = mg \qquad (29.9)$$

with the initial conditions

$$\left.\begin{array}{l} x(0) = 0 \\ \dot{x}(0) = \sqrt{2gh} \end{array}\right\} \qquad (29.10)$$

With the substitutions

$$\omega = \sqrt{\frac{k}{m}}$$

$$\frac{c}{m} = 2 \frac{c}{2\sqrt{km}} \sqrt{\frac{k}{m}} = 2\alpha\omega$$

Fig. 46

the subsidiary equation and its inverse become

$$\bar{x}(s) = \frac{\sqrt{2gh}}{s^2 + 2\alpha\omega s + \omega^2} + \frac{g}{s(s^2 + 2\alpha\omega s + \omega^2)} \qquad (29.11)$$

$$\left.\begin{array}{l} x(t) = \dfrac{\sqrt{2gh}}{\omega\sqrt{1-\alpha^2}}\, e^{-\alpha\omega t} \sin \omega\sqrt{1-\alpha^2}\, t \\[2mm] \qquad + \dfrac{g\, e^{-\alpha\omega t}}{\omega^2\sqrt{1-\alpha^2}} \sin(\omega\sqrt{1-\alpha^2}\, t - \gamma) + \dfrac{g}{\omega^2} \\[2mm] \qquad\qquad \gamma = \tan^{-1}\dfrac{\sqrt{1-\alpha^2}}{\alpha} \end{array}\right\} \qquad (29.12)$$

We shall now assume that the statical deflection g/ω^2 is negligible compared to the dynamical deflection, in which case only the first term of $x(t)$ is retained.   The acceleration can be readily obtained by applying the differentiation formula

$$\frac{d^2 uv}{dt^2} = u \frac{d^2 v}{dt^2} + v \frac{d^2 u}{dt^2} + 2 \frac{du}{dt}\frac{dv}{dt}$$

to Eq. (29.12).   Thus

$$\left.\begin{array}{l} \ddot{x}(t) = \dfrac{-\sqrt{2gh}}{\omega\sqrt{1-\alpha^2}}\, \{[\omega^2(1-\alpha^2) - \alpha^2\omega^2]\sin\omega\sqrt{1-\alpha^2}\, t \\[2mm] \qquad\qquad + 2\alpha\omega^2\sqrt{1-\alpha^2}\cos\omega\sqrt{1-\alpha^2}\, t\}\, e^{-\alpha\omega t} \\[2mm] \quad = \dfrac{-\omega\sqrt{2gh}}{\sqrt{1-\alpha^2}}\, e^{-\alpha\omega t}\cos(\omega\sqrt{1-\alpha^2}\, t + \varphi) \\[2mm] \qquad\qquad \varphi = \tan^{-1}\dfrac{2\alpha^2 - 1}{2\alpha\sqrt{1-\alpha^2}} \end{array}\right\} \qquad (29.13)$$

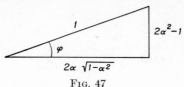

FIG. 47

For purposes of plotting, it is convenient to express Eq. 29.13 in nondimensional form as follows:

$$\frac{-\ddot{x}(t)}{g\sqrt{2h/\delta_{\text{st}}}} = \frac{e^{-\alpha\omega t}}{\sqrt{1-\alpha^2}}\cos(\omega\sqrt{1-\alpha^2}\,t+\varphi) \qquad (29.14)$$

This equation is plotted in Fig. 48 for various values of the damping factor $\alpha = c/c_{\text{cr}}$. The curves show that the maximum acceleration occurs at $t = 0$ for $\alpha \geq 0.50$. For $\alpha < 0.50$, the maximum acceleration occurs after $t = 0$.

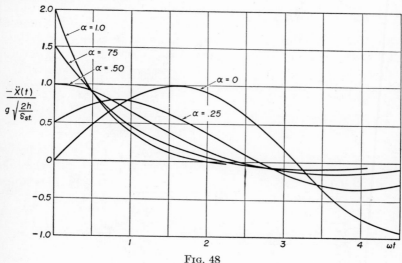

FIG. 48

Problems

91. Obtain Eq. (29.13) by evaluating the inversion of the subsidiary equation

$$\ddot{x}(s) = \frac{s^2\sqrt{2gh}}{s^2+2\alpha\omega s+\omega^2} = \frac{s^2\sqrt{2gh}}{(s-s_1)(s-s_2)}$$
$$= 2\mathcal{g}\left\{\frac{s_1^2\,e^{s_1 t}}{s_1-s_2}\right\}\sqrt{2gh}$$

where $s_{1,2} = (-\alpha \pm i\sqrt{1-\alpha^2})\omega$ and $\mathscr{I}\{\quad\}$ stands for the imaginary part of the quantity $\{\quad\}$.

92. An article m, spring-supported in a box as shown in Fig. 49, has a natural frequency of 2 cps. Determine the maximum acceleration developed when the box is dropped through a height of 8 ft with no rebound.

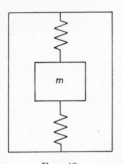

FIG. 49

93. If damping is introduced in Prob. 92 so that $\alpha = 0.25$, determine the maximum acceleration developed.

94. If a body is spring-supported with a statical deflection of $\delta_{st} = 0.30$ in., how far can it be dropped without exceeding an acceleration of 4 g? If damping of $\alpha = 0.75$ is introduced, what will be the maximum height of drop?

30. Shock Testing. The mechanical ruggedness of instruments or equipment is frequently determined by high-impact shock tests. This is particularly true of military equipment which must stand up under severe mechanical shocks.

Figure 50 shows a schematic diagram of a standard shock testing machine. H represents an impact hammer which imparts the energy to the supporting base m_1, referred to as the *impact table*.

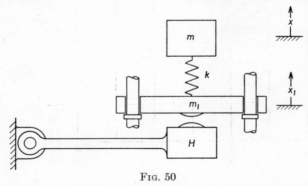

FIG. 50

The test specimen m, representing the equipment to be tested, is supported by the coupling spring k.

In general, the mass m of the equipment to be tested is small compared with that of the impact table, and hence the impact of the hammer is assumed to act on a free mass m_1, giving it a velocity $\dot{x}_1$. The problem then resolves itself to one of determining the acceleration of m due to a prescribed motion of the lower end of the spring under impact of the hammer H.

It is found that for medium-high-impact shock machines that the impact force of the hammer is very nearly triangular in distribu-

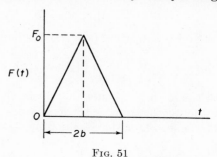

Fig. 51

tion,* as shown in Fig. 51. The equation for such a pulse can be readily written as

$$F(t) = \frac{F_0 t}{b} [\mathfrak{u}(t) - \mathfrak{u}(t - b)]$$

$$+ \left(2F_0 - \frac{F_0 t}{b}\right) [\mathfrak{u}(t - b) - \mathfrak{u}(t - 2b)] \quad (30.1)$$

and its transform after simplification reduces to

$$\bar{F}(s) = \frac{F_0}{b} \left(\frac{1 - e^{-bs}}{s}\right)^2 \quad (30.2)$$

For the free mass m_1 which is initially at rest, we have the differential equation

$$m_1 \ddot{x}_1 = F(t) \quad (30.3)$$

with its transform

$$s^2 m_1 \bar{x}_1(s) = \frac{F_0}{b} \left(\frac{1 - e^{-bs}}{s}\right)^2$$

or

$$\bar{x}_1(s) = \frac{F_0}{b m_1 s^2} \left(\frac{1 - e^{-bs}}{s}\right)^2 \quad (30.4)$$

The motion of the impact table can be determined by the inverse of the last equation but is not necessary for this problem.

* J. T. Muller, "Transients in Mechanical Systems," *Bell System Tech. Jour.*, **27**, 4 (October 1948), pages 657–683.

We next consider the equation of motion of m, which is

$$m\ddot{x} = k(x_1 - x) \tag{30.5}$$

The subsidiary equation then becomes

$$\bar{x}(s)[ms^2 + k] = k\bar{x}_1(s)$$

Letting $\omega^2 = k/m$ and substituting for $\bar{x}_1(s)$, we have

$$\bar{x}(s) = \frac{\omega^2}{s^2 + \omega^2} \frac{F_0}{bm_1 s^2} \left(\frac{1 - e^{-bs}}{s}\right)^2 \tag{30.6}$$

It should be noted here that it is not the displacement which is of interest; rather, the acceleration of m determines the severity of the test. If we let a stand for the acceleration, $\bar{a}(s) = s^2\bar{x}(s)$, or

$$\bar{a}(s) = \frac{F_0}{bm_1} \frac{\omega^2}{s^2 + \omega^2} \left(\frac{1 - e^{-bs}}{s}\right)^2 \tag{30.7}$$

The inverse transformation results in the acceleration equation

$$a(t) = \frac{F_0\omega^2}{bm_1} \left\{ \left(\frac{t}{\omega^2} - \frac{\sin \omega t}{\omega^3}\right) - 2\left[\frac{(t - b)}{\omega^2} - \frac{\sin \omega(t - b)}{\omega^3}\right] \mathfrak{u}(t - b) \right.$$
$$\left. + \left[\frac{(t - 2b)}{\omega^2} - \frac{\sin \omega(t - 2b)}{\omega^3}\right] \mathfrak{u}(t - 2b) \right\} \tag{30.8}$$

This equation can be reduced to nondimensional form by the following substitution:

$$\frac{F_0}{m_1} = \text{maximum acceleration of impact table}$$

$$\frac{a}{a_1} = \frac{m_1 a(t)}{F_0} = \text{ratio of acceleration of } m \text{ to that of } m_1$$

$$\tau = \frac{t}{2b} = \text{elapsed time expressed as a ratio of pulse}$$
$$\text{length}$$

Thus

$$\frac{a}{a_1} = \left\{ \left(2\tau - \frac{1}{b\omega} \sin 2b\omega\tau\right) \right.$$
$$- 2\left[(2\tau - 1) - \frac{1}{b\omega} \sin b\omega(2\tau - 1)\right] \mathfrak{u}(2\tau - 1)$$
$$\left. + \left[2(\tau - 1) - \frac{1}{b\omega} \sin 2b\omega(\tau - 1)\right] \mathfrak{u}(\tau - 1) \right\} \quad (0 < \tau < \infty) \tag{30.9}$$

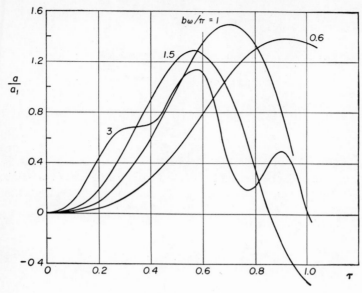

FIG. 52

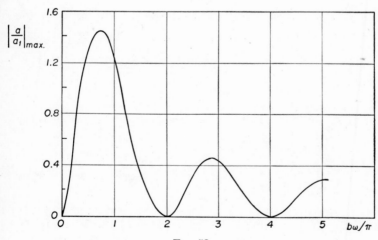

FIG. 53

which holds for all values of τ. For $\tau > 1$ the above terms add up to the following:

$$\frac{a}{a_1} = \frac{-1}{b\omega} \{\sin 2b\omega\tau - 2 \sin b\omega(2\tau - 1) + \sin 2b\omega(\tau - 1)\}$$

$$= \frac{2}{b\omega} (1 - \cos b\omega) \sin b\omega(2\tau - 1) \qquad (\tau > 1) \quad (30.10)$$

which shows that the acceleration ratio is sinusoidal with an amplitude equal to

$$\left|\frac{a}{a_1}\right|_{\max} = \frac{2}{b\omega} (1 - \cos b\omega) \tag{30.11}$$

A plot of Eqs. (30.9) and (30.11) is given in Figs. 52 and 53:

Problems

95. A spring-supported system of Fig. 54 is excited by a series of

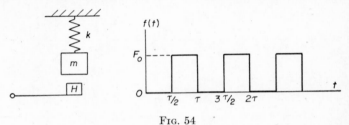

FIG. 54

blows by H. If this force is represented by rectangular pulses, show that

$$\bar{f}(s) = \frac{F_0\, e^{-\frac{s\tau}{2}}}{s(1 + e^{-\frac{s\tau}{2}})}$$

$$\bar{x}(s) = \frac{F_0}{ms} \frac{e^{-\frac{s\tau}{2}}}{(1 + e^{-\frac{s\tau}{2}})(s^2 + \omega^2)}$$

$$x(t) = \frac{F_0}{m\omega^2} \left\{\left[1 - \cos \omega\left(t - \frac{\tau}{2}\right)\right] \mathfrak{u}\left(t - \frac{\tau}{2}\right)\right.$$

$$- [1 - \cos \omega(t - \tau)]\mathfrak{u}(t - \tau)$$

$$\left. + \left[1 - \cos \omega\left(t - \frac{3\tau}{2}\right)\right] \mathfrak{u}\left(t - \frac{3\tau}{2}\right) - \cdots\right\}$$

96. Determine the displacement and acceleration of the impact table due to a triangular force pulse of maximum value F_0 and duration $2b$.

Show that the displacement after $t = 2b$ is

$$x_1(t) = \frac{F_0 b}{m_1}(t - b)$$

97. The velocity of an impact table weighing 800 lb was measured to be 8 ft/sec for $t > 2b$. Assuming the force pulse to be triangular and of duration 100 microseconds, determine (a) the acceleration $a_1 = F_0/m_1$ and (b) the maximum force.

$Ans.$ $F_0/m_1 = 160,000$ ft/sec^2; $F_0 = 3.97 \times 10^6$ lb.

98. In Prob. 97, what maximum acceleration is developed by the test specimen if it is supported to have a natural frequency of 2000 cps?

99. Develop an equation for the ratio a/a_1 for a rectangular force pulse of duration b.

31. The Rate of Roll of an Airplane. The rolling motion of an airplane due to lateral control displacement can be approximated by the following differential equation:

$$I\ddot{\theta} + D\dot{\theta} = Mx(t) \tag{31.1}$$

where

   I = moment of inertia of the airplane about the longitudinal axes,

   D = damping moment of wings per unit rolling velocity,

   θ = angle of roll,

   $Mx(t)$ = rolling moment due to lateral control displacement $x(t)$.

We shall assume that the control displacement $x(t)$ has the form shown in Fig. 55. Letting $p = \dot{\theta}$ be the rate of roll, we can rewrite

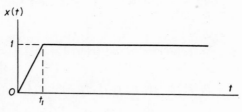

Fig. 55

the differential equation as

$$\left.\begin{aligned} Ip + Dp &= M_0 \frac{t}{t_1} \quad (0 < t < t_1) \\ &= M_0 \qquad\quad (t > t_1) \end{aligned}\right\} \tag{31.2}$$

The corresponding subsidiary equations are

$$\bar{p}(s) = \frac{M_0}{It_1} \frac{1}{s^2(s + D/I)} \qquad\qquad (0 < t < t_1) \left.\begin{matrix}\\ \\\end{matrix}\right\}$$
$$= \frac{M_0}{I} \frac{1}{s(s + D/I)} + \frac{p(t_1)}{(s + D/I)} \quad (t > t_1) \qquad (31.3)$$

from which

$$p(t) = \frac{M_0}{D} \frac{t}{t_1} - \frac{M_0 I}{D^2 t_1} (1 - e^{-\frac{D}{I}t}) \qquad\qquad (0 < t < t_1) \quad (31.4)$$

$$= \frac{M_0}{D} [1 - e^{-\frac{D}{I}(t-t_1)}] + p(t_1) e^{-\frac{D}{I}(t-t_1)} \qquad (t > t_1) \quad (31.5)$$

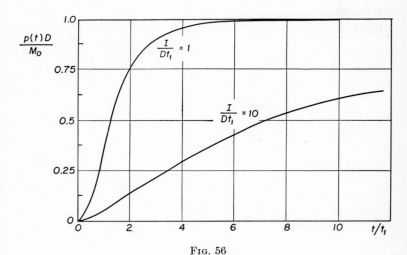

$$\frac{p(t)D}{M_0}$$

$$\frac{I}{Dt_1} = 1$$

$$\frac{I}{Dt_1} = 10$$

FIG. 56

The quantity $p(t_1)$ can be evaluated from Eq. (31.4) at $t = t_1$.

$$p(t_1) = \frac{M_0}{D} - \frac{M_0 I}{D^2 t_1} (1 - e^{-\frac{D}{I}t_1})$$

Thus Eq. (31.5) reduces to the form

$$p(t) = \frac{M_0}{D} - \frac{M_0 I}{D^2 t_1} (1 - e^{-\frac{D}{I}t_1}) e^{-\frac{D}{I}(t-t_1)} \qquad (31.6)$$

These equations can be expressed in the following nondimensional form

$$\frac{p(t)D}{M_0} = \frac{t}{t_1} - \left(\frac{I}{Dt_1}\right)[1 - e^{-\left(\frac{Dt_1}{I}\right)\frac{t}{t_1}}] \qquad (0 < t < t_1) \quad (31.7)$$

$$= 1 - \left(\frac{I}{Dt_1}\right)[1 - e^{-\left(\frac{Dt_1}{I}\right)}] e^{-\left(\frac{Dt_1}{I}\right)\left(\frac{t}{t_1}-1\right)} \qquad (t > t_1) \quad (31.8)$$

which is plotted in Fig. 56 with I/Dt_1 as a parameter. The elementary discussion presented neglects the loss of rolling moment due to structural twist of the wings.*

Problem

100. Determine the rate of roll of an airplane when the control displacement $x(t)$ is a unit step function.

32. Servomechanism. The purpose of a continuous control servo system is to regulate the position θ_0 of an output load device

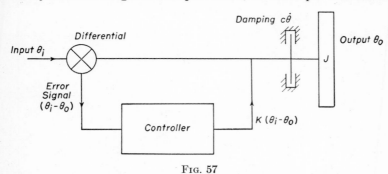

FIG. 57

to follow rapidly and accurately the position θ_i of a control input device. A servomechanism compares the input and output positions and translates any discrepancy between these into an error signal $(\theta_i - \theta_0)$, which in turn acts on the output to minimize this discrepancy.

The principle of the servomechanism can be illustrated in terms of the rotational system of Fig. 57, where the displacement θ_0 of a body of moment of inertia J is to be in agreement with the input displacement θ_i. The error $(\theta_i - \theta_0)$ between the input and output is detected by a differential and fed into a controller, which in turn applies a correcting torque $K(\theta_i - \theta_0)$ to the output shaft. Usually damping is provided in one form or another to prevent undesirable

* W. T. Thomson, "Rate of Roll of Airplanes," *Aircraft Engineering*, January 1947.

oscillation of the system. The simplest arrangement consists of a damping torque $c\dot{\theta}_0$ proportional to the output velocity. Thus the torque applied to the output shaft is $K(\theta_i - \theta_0) - c\dot{\theta}_0$, and the differential equation of motion for the driven body becomes

$$J\ddot{\theta}_0 = K(\theta_i - \theta_0) - c\dot{\theta}_0$$

which can be rearranged as

$$J\ddot{\theta}_0 + c\dot{\theta}_0 + K\theta_0 = K\theta_i \tag{32.1}$$

If the system is at rest at $t = 0$, we have $\theta_0(0) = \dot{\theta}_0(0) = 0$, and the subsidiary equation becomes

$$\bar{\theta}_0(s) = \frac{K\bar{\theta}_i(s)}{J\left(s^2 + \dfrac{c}{J}s + \dfrac{K}{J}\right)} \tag{32.2}$$

If the control input is given a uniform motion $\theta_i = \Omega t$, then $\bar{\theta}_i(s) = \Omega/s^2$, and Eq. (32.2) becomes

$$\bar{\theta}_0(s) = \frac{K\Omega}{Js^2\left(s^2 + \dfrac{c}{J}s + \dfrac{K}{J}\right)} = \frac{\Omega}{s^2} - \frac{c\Omega}{Ks} + \frac{\Omega\left(\dfrac{c}{K}s + \dfrac{c^2}{KJ} - 1\right)}{s^2 + \dfrac{c}{J}s + \dfrac{K}{J}} \tag{32.3}$$

Hence the inverse transform is (see Example 10.1)

$$\theta_0(t) = \Omega t - \frac{c\Omega}{K} + \frac{\Omega}{\beta}e^{-\frac{c}{2J}t}\sin(\beta t - \varphi) \tag{32.4}$$

where
$$\beta^2 = \frac{K}{J} - \left(\frac{c}{2J}\right)^2$$

$$\alpha = \left(\frac{c}{2J}\right)$$

$$\varphi = \tan^{-1}\frac{2\alpha\beta}{\beta^2 - \alpha^2}$$

Thus the error signal $\theta_i - \theta_0$ is given by the equation

$$\theta_i - \theta_0 = \frac{c\Omega}{K} - \frac{\Omega}{\beta}e^{-\frac{c}{2J}t}\sin(\beta t - \varphi) \tag{32.5}$$

which is plotted in Fig. 58. It is evident, then, that the error signal consists of a constant lag $c\Omega/K$ and a transient term.

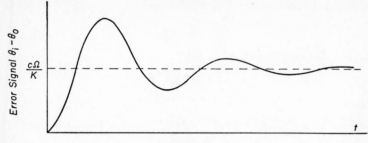

FIG. 58

33. Electrically Controlled Servo System. Figure 59 shows a servo system which is controlled electrically. M is a motor supplying torque T_m to the rotating system of total moment of inertia J. N is a tachometer which absorbs negligible torque and generates a feedback voltage $E_n = k_n \dot{\theta}$, where $\dot{\theta}$ is the rotational speed of the system. A is a vacuum-tube amplifier with a gain μ. The input voltage e to the amplifier is the difference between the applied

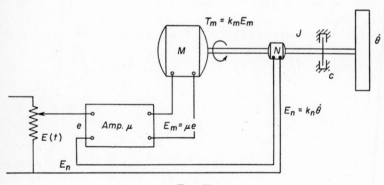

FIG. 59

control voltage $E(t)$ and the tachometer voltage E_n, and its output voltage μe is applied to the motor M. Thus when the motor is running under steady-state conditions, $e = E(t) - E_n$ is just sufficient for the motor torque $T_m = k_m E_m$ to overcome the damping torque $c\dot{\theta}$.

Equating the torque of the motor to the torque necessary to accelerate the system and overcome friction, we find that the differential equation for the system becomes

$$J\ddot{\theta} + c\dot{\theta} = \mu k_m[E(t) - k_n\dot{\theta}] \tag{33.1}$$

which can be rearranged as

$$J\ddot{\theta} + R\dot{\theta} = \mu k_m E(t) \tag{33.2}$$

where $\qquad\qquad R = (c + \mu k_n k_m)$

Thus the subsidiary equation for the speed is

$$\bar{\dot{\theta}}(s) = \frac{\mu k_m \bar{E}(s)}{J(s + R/J)} + \frac{\dot{\theta}(0)}{(s + R/J)} \tag{33.3}$$

In this equation $\bar{E}(s)$ is the transform of the applied control voltage $E(t)$, and $\dot{\theta}(0)$ is the speed of the system at $t = 0$.

We shall now assume that the system is running at a speed $\dot{\theta}(0)$ with a control voltage E_0, and this speed is to be modified by increasing the control voltage linearly according to the equation $E_0\Omega t$. Then

$$E(t) = E_0(1 + \Omega t) \quad\text{and}\quad \bar{E}(s) = E_0\left(\frac{1}{s} + \frac{\Omega}{s^2}\right)$$

When we substitute into Eq. 33.3, the subsidiary equation becomes

$$\bar{\dot{\theta}}(s) = \frac{\mu k_m E_0}{Js(s + R/J)} + \frac{\mu k_m E_0 \Omega}{Js^2(s + R/J)} + \frac{\dot{\theta}(0)}{(s + R/J)} \tag{33.4}$$

The solution after rearranging terms is then

$$\dot{\theta}(t) = \frac{\mu k_m E_0}{R}\left(1 - \frac{\Omega J}{R}\right) + \frac{\mu k_m E_0 \Omega t}{R}$$

$$+ \left[\dot{\theta}(0) - \frac{\mu k_m E_0 \Omega J}{R^2} - \frac{\mu k_m E_0}{R}\right]e^{-\frac{Rt}{J}} \tag{33.5}$$

It should be noted that the last term in this equation contains the factor $e^{-\frac{Rt}{J}}$ and hence is the transient term. Since $R = (c + \mu k_n k_m)$, the effect of feedback is to increase the stability of the system by causing the transient term to vanish rapidly.

Problems

101. If critical damping is employed in the servo system of Fig. 57, show that the error becomes a steady value of $c\Omega/K$.

102. If for the servo system of Fig. 57 the damping is taken equal to $c(\theta_i - \theta_0)$, show that the solution for the error signal is

$$\theta_i - \theta_0 = -\frac{\Omega}{\beta} e^{-\frac{c}{2J}t} \sin \beta t$$

which contains no permanent lag.

103. The system of Fig. 59 is rotating at a constant speed θ_0 with an input voltage $E(t) = E_0$. To change the speed of rotation, the input rheostat is turned at a constant rate to a new position in time t_1 such that

$$E(t) = E_0(1 + \Omega t)\mathfrak{U}(t) - E_0\Omega(t - t_1)\mathfrak{U}(t - t_1)$$

Determine the equation for the speed $\dot{\theta}(t)$.

104. Figure 60 shows a motor generator set, the rotating system of which is represented by the moment of inertias I_m and I_G and the torsional

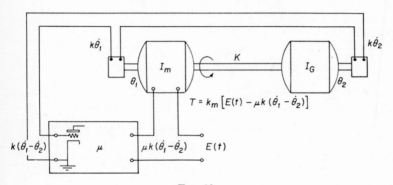

Fɪɢ. 60

stiffness K of the shaft. To reduce the torsional oscillation between the two units, a servo system consisting of two identical tachometers is connected in opposition. The resulting voltage is amplified and placed in series to oppose the line voltage $E(t)$ so that the motor torque is $k_m[E(t) - \mu k(\dot{\theta}_1 - \dot{\theta}_2)]$. Show that the equation of motion for the torsional oscillation of the system is

$$I_m I_G\ddot{\varphi} + \mu k k_m I_G\dot{\varphi} + K(I_m + I_G)\varphi = k_m I_G E(t)$$

where
$$\varphi = \theta_1 - \theta_2$$

105. If in the system of Fig. 60 the tachometers are disconnected and a constant torque T_0 is developed by the motor with the system initially at rest, show that

$$\dot{\theta}_2(t) = \frac{T_0}{I_m + I_G}\left(t - \frac{1}{\omega}\sin \omega t\right)$$

where

$$\omega = \sqrt{\frac{K(I_m + I_G)}{I_m I_G}}$$

34. The Electromechanical System. A vibrating system frequently includes interacting mechanical and electrical elements. For instance, if a conductor of length l moves with velocity $\dot{x}$ in a uniform magnetic field B, a voltage given by the equation

$$E = Bl\dot{x} \tag{34.1}$$

is induced.

Conversely, the same conductor carrying a current i experiences a mechanical force

$$F = Bli \tag{34.2}$$

It is standard practice in dealing with electromechanical problems to use the MKS system of units, which eliminates cumbersome

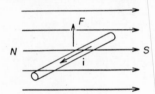 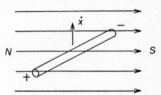

Fig. 61

conversion factors. Thus the quantities above are defined as follows:

E = volts,

i = amperes,

F = force in newtons,

$\dot{x}$ = velocity perpendicular to magnetic field in meters per second,

B = magnetic flux density in webers per square meter,

l = length of conductor perpendicular to B in meters.

The direction of the force and induced voltage is established by reference to Fig. 61(a) and (b).

EXAMPLE 34.1: Determine the time required for the electromagnetic switch of Fig. 62 to close. On the assumption that the coil impedance is a pure inductance, the electrical and mechanical equations become

$$E_0 \mathcal{U}(t) = L \frac{di}{dt} + Bl\dot{x}$$

$$m\ddot{x} = -c\dot{x} - kx + Bli$$

With initial values $\dot{x}(0) = i(0) = 0$, the transform of these equa-

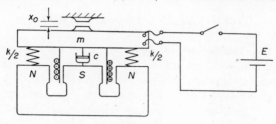

FIG. 62

tions can be written as

$$\frac{E_0}{s} = Ls\bar{\imath}(s) + Bls\bar{x}(s)$$

$$ms^2\bar{x}(s) = -cs\bar{x}(s) - k\bar{x}(s) + Bl\bar{\imath}(s)$$

Eliminating $\bar{\imath}(s)$ and solving for $\bar{x}(s)$, we obtain

$$\bar{x}(s) = \frac{E_0 Bl}{Lms^2 \left[s^2 + \frac{c}{m} s + \frac{k}{m} + \frac{B^2 l^2}{Lm} \right]}$$

If we let

$$\frac{c}{m} = 2\alpha \quad \text{and} \quad \frac{k}{m} + \frac{B^2 l^2}{Lm} = \omega^2$$

the inverse of the above equation is

$$x(t) = \frac{E_0 Bl}{Lm\omega^2} \left\{ t - \frac{2\alpha}{\omega^2} + \frac{e^{-\alpha t}}{\beta} \sin (\beta t + \varphi) \right\}$$

where

$$\beta^2 = \omega^2 - \alpha^2 \quad \text{and} \quad \varphi = \tan^{-1} \frac{2\alpha\beta}{\alpha^2 - \beta^2}$$

The time t_1, corresponding to the gap displacement x_0 can then be obtained by plotting the right side of this equation and finding t_1 when $x(t) = x_0$.

Problems

106. Determine the current $i(t)$ in the coil for the system of Fig. 62.

107. In Fig. 62 add a resistor R in series with E and determine the equation for the displacement $x(t)$.

CHAPTER 4

Structural Applications

35. Statical Deflection of Beams. The operational method offers a very simple approach to the beam problem. In contrast to the classical method, which requires equations to be written for each interval between loads, the operational method enables any loading to be accounted for by a single equation in terms of boundary values at the origin. For such problems the time coordinate t is replaced by the space coordinate x. Beams with abrupt changes in cross section offer no unusual difficulties to the operational method.

36. General Beam Equation. The differential equation for the loading of a uniform beam is

$$EI \frac{d^4 y}{dx^4} = f(x) \tag{36.1}$$

where $f(x)$ represents the loading (load/unit length), considered positive in the upward direction. If we take the Laplace transform of Eq. (36.1) with x as the independent variable, the subsidiary equation for the deflection becomes

$$\bar{y}(s) = \frac{y(0)}{s} + \frac{y'(0)}{s^2} + \frac{y''(0)}{s^3} + \frac{y'''(0)}{s^4} + \frac{1}{EI} \frac{\bar{f}(s)}{s^4} \tag{36.2}$$

From its inverse, the deflection can be written as

$$y(x) = y(0) + y'(0)x + y''(0) \frac{x^2}{2!} + y'''(0) \frac{x^3}{3!} + \frac{1}{EI} \mathcal{L}^{-1} \frac{\bar{f}(s)}{s^4} \tag{36.3}$$

where

$y(0)$ = deflection at $x = 0$,

$y'(0) = \left(\dfrac{dy}{dx}\right)_{x=0}$ = slope at $x = 0$,

$y''(0) = \dfrac{M(0)}{EI} = \dfrac{1}{EI} \times$ moment at $x = 0$,

$y'''(0) = \dfrac{V(0)}{EI} = \dfrac{1}{EI} \times$ shear at $x = 0$.

In general, some of these quantities are known. The remaining unknown quantities at $x = 0$ are then evaluated from known deflection, slope, moment, or shear at some other point along the beam.

37. Beam Loading. Beam loading $f(x)$ can be expressed operationally, as has been discussed in Chapter 2. A distributed load can be started and stopped at any position x_1 and x_2 by multiplying its equation by the unit step function $[\mathfrak{U}(x - x_1) - \mathfrak{U}(x - x_2)]$,

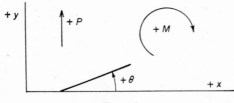

FIG. 63

which is unity between x_1 and x_2 and zero everywhere else. The loading corresponding to a concentrated load P at $x = x_1$ is $P\mathfrak{U}'(x - x_1)$, whereas the loading corresponding to a couple M at x_1 is $M\mathfrak{U}''(x - x_1)$.

The sign convention adopted for the beam problem is shown in Fig. 63. The problem then resolves into one of writing down the quantity $\mathcal{L}^{-1}\bar{f}(s)/s^4$ and evaluating the unknown quantities at $x = 0$ from known values at some other point along the beam.

EXAMPLE 37.1: Determine the equation for the deflection of the simply supported beam with a concentrated load at $x = a$ as shown in Fig. 64.

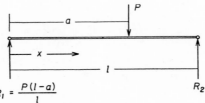

FIG. 64

The loading for this case is

$$f(x) = -P\mathfrak{U}'(x - a)$$

and its transform and contribution to the deflection are (see second shifting theorem, Section 17)

$$f(s) = -P e^{-as}$$

$$\mathcal{L}^{-1} \frac{\bar{f}(s)}{s^4} = -P \frac{(x-a)^\circ}{3!} \mathfrak{U}(x-a)$$

Substituting into Eq. (36.3) with $y(0) = y''(0) = 0$ and $y'''(0) = R_1/EI$, we obtain

$$y(x) = y'(0)x + R_1 \frac{x^3}{6EI} - \frac{P}{6EI} (x-a)^3 \mathfrak{U}(x-a)$$

From the boundary condition $y(l) = 0$, we obtain

$$y'(0) = - \frac{R_1 l^2}{6EI} + \frac{P}{6EI} \frac{(l-a)^3}{l}$$

and the final equation for the deflection becomes

$$y(x) = \left[\frac{-R_1 l^3 + P(l-a)^3}{6EIl} \right] x + \frac{R_1 x^3}{6EI} - \frac{P(x-a)^3}{6EI} \mathfrak{U}(x-a)$$

Since $\mathfrak{U}(x-a) = 0$ for $x < a$ and unity for $x > a$, the last term is retained only for the right side of the load P.

38. Nonuniform Beam.   There are two ways of treating beams with more than one cross section operationally.   In the first method, the beam is reduced to one of uniform cross section with modified loads so that the M/EI curve is the same as that of the original beam.*   The treatment of the problem after this modification is then identical to that of the previous section.   In the second method,† the moment equation is used instead of the loading equation, and the change in the stiffness is accounted for by a function of the form

$$\frac{1}{EI} [1 + k\mathfrak{U}(x-a)]$$

To illustrate the first method, consider the beam shown in Fig. 65(a).   It is possible to reduce this beam to one of uniform stiffness EI_1 with the modified loading shown in Fig. 65(b).   To determine the modified load, we can write the following M/I equa-

---

* M. Hetenyi, "Deflection of Beams of Varying Cross Section," *Jour. of Applied Mech.*, **4**, 2 (June 1937), pages A49–52.

W. T. Thomson, "Deflection of Beams by the Operational Method," *Jour. of Franklin Inst.*, **247**, 6 (June 1949), pages 557–568.

† Carslow and Jaeger, *Operational Methods in Applied Mathematics*, Oxford University Press, 1941, page 327.

tion with $x = a$ as the reference.

$$\frac{M_{x'}}{I_2} = \frac{1}{I_2}\left(M_a + V_a x' - \frac{wx'^2}{2}\right)$$

$$= \frac{1}{I_1}\left[M_a + V_a x' - \frac{wx'^2}{2} - M_a\left(1 - \frac{I_1}{I_2}\right) - V_a\left(1 - \frac{I_1}{I_2}\right)x'\right.$$

$$\left. + w\left(1 - \frac{I_1}{I_2}\right)\frac{x'^2}{2}\right] \quad (38.1)$$

It is evident from this equation that the modified loads given by

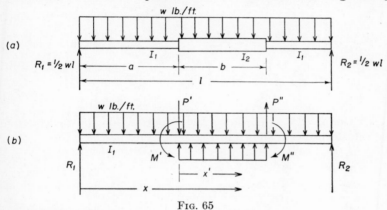

w lb./ft.

(a)

$R_1 = \frac{1}{2} wl$ I_1 I_2 I_1 $R_2 = \frac{1}{2} wl$

a b l

w lb./ft. P' P''

(b)

R_1 I_1 M' M'' R_2

x'

x

Fig. 65

its last three terms are

$$M' = M_a\left(1 - \frac{I_1}{I_2}\right)$$

$$P' = V_a\left(1 - \frac{I_1}{I_2}\right) \quad (38.2)$$

$$q = w\left(1 - \frac{I_1}{I_2}\right)$$

The loads P'' and M'' are then determined from the fact that the modified loads must be in equilibrium by themselves:

$$P'' = P' - qb = (V_a - wb)\left(1 - \frac{I_1}{I_2}\right) = V_b\left(1 - \frac{I_1}{I_2}\right)$$

$$M'' = M' + P'b - \frac{qb^2}{2} = \left(M_a + V_a b - \frac{wb^2}{2}\right)\left(1 - \frac{I_1}{I_2}\right) \quad (38.3)$$

$$= M_b\left(1 - \frac{I_1}{I_2}\right)$$

By using the method of the previous section, we find that the loading equation must include the following additional terms due to the modified loads:

$$f(x) = q[\mathcal{U}(x - a) - \mathcal{U}(x - a - b)] - P'\mathcal{U}'(x - a)$$
$$- M'\mathcal{U}''(x - a) + P''\mathcal{U}'(x - a - b) + M''\mathcal{U}''(x - a - b) \quad (38.4)$$

Hence its transform and contribution to the deflection are

$$\bar{f}(s) = q\left(\frac{e^{-as} - e^{-(a+b)s}}{s}\right) - P'\,e^{-as} - M's\,e^{-as}$$
$$+ P''\,e^{-(a+b)s} + M''s\,e^{-(a+b)s} \quad (38.5)$$

$$\mathcal{L}^{-1}\frac{\bar{f}(s)}{s^4} = \left[\frac{q(x - a)^4}{4!} - \frac{P'(x - a)^3}{3!} - \frac{M'(x - a)^2}{2!}\right]\mathcal{U}(x - a)$$
$$+ \left[\frac{-q(x - a - b)^4}{4!} + \frac{P''(x - a - b)^3}{3!} + \frac{M''(x - a - b)^2}{2!}\right]$$
$$\mathcal{U}(x - a - b) \quad (38.6)$$

EXAMPLE 38.1: Determine the equation for the deflection of the cantilever beam shown in Fig. 66(a).

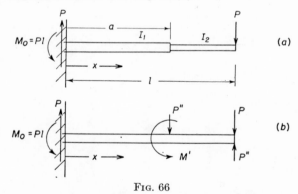

FIG. 66

The equivalent uniform beam with its modified loads are shown in Fig. 66(b). Thus from Eq. (38.2),

$$P' = P\left(1 - \frac{I_1}{I_2}\right)$$

$$M' = -P(l - a)\left(1 - \frac{I_1}{I_2}\right)$$

The loading, its transform, and its contribution to the deflection then become

$$f(x) = -P'\mathfrak{u}'(x - a) - M'\mathfrak{u}''(x - a)$$
$$\bar{f}(s) = -P' e^{-as} - M's e^{-as}$$
$$\frac{\mathcal{L}^{-1}\bar{f}(s)}{s^4} = \left[\frac{-P(x - a)^3}{3!} + P(l - a)\frac{(x - a)^2}{2!}\right]\left(1 - \frac{I_1}{I_2}\right)\mathfrak{u}(x - a)$$

Substituting into the deflection equation with $y(0) = y'(0) = 0$, $y''(0) = -Pl/EI_1$, and $y'''(0) = P/EI_1$, we obtain

$$EI_1 y(x) = -\frac{Plx^2}{2!} + \frac{Px^3}{3!}$$
$$+ \left[\frac{-P(x - a)^3}{3!} + \frac{P(l - a)(x - a)^2}{2!}\right]\left(1 - \frac{I_1}{I_2}\right)\mathfrak{u}(x - a)$$

If we let $x = l$ the deflection at the end becomes

$$y(l) = \frac{1}{EI_1}\left[-\frac{Pl^3}{3} + \frac{P(l - a)^3}{3}\left(1 - \frac{I_1}{I_2}\right)\right]$$

For the second approach to the problem, we start with the moment equation

$$\frac{d^2y}{dx^2} = \frac{M}{EI_1}[1 - k\mathfrak{u}(x - a)]$$

where $1/EI$ over the section $0 \leq x \leq a$ is $1/EI_1$ and that over the section $x \geq a$ is

$$\frac{1}{EI_1}(1 - k) = \frac{1}{EI_2}$$

Solving for k, we have

$$k = \left(1 - \frac{I_1}{I_2}\right)$$

As an illustration, we shall use the preceding example of the cantilever beam, for which the differential equation is

$$\frac{d^2y}{dx^2} = \frac{-P(l - x)}{EI_1}[1 - k\mathfrak{u}(x - a)]$$

The subsidiary equation with $y(0) = y'(0) = 0$ becomes

$$EI_1 s^2 \bar{y}(s) = -\frac{Pl}{s} + \frac{P}{s^2} + \frac{Plk\, e^{-as}}{s} - Pk\, e^{-as}\left(\frac{a}{s} + \frac{1}{s^2}\right)$$

where
$$\mathcal{L}x\mathfrak{u}(x - a) = e^{-as}\left(\frac{a}{s} + \frac{1}{s^2}\right)$$

Taking the inverse transformation, we obtain

$$EI_1 y(x) = -\frac{Plx^2}{2} + \frac{Px^3}{6}$$
$$+ Pk \left[\frac{l(x-a)^2}{2} - \frac{(x-a)^3}{6} - \frac{a(x-a)^2}{2} \right] \mathfrak{u}(x-a)$$

which agrees with the previous result.

Problems

108. Determine the deflection equation for a cantilever beam with a uniform load over the outer half of the span.

109. Determine the operational solution for the beam of Fig. 67.

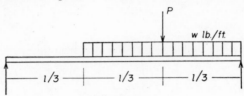

FIG. 67

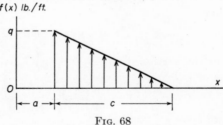

FIG. 68

110. Show that the transform of the triangular load shown in Fig. 68 is

$$\bar{f}(s) = q \left(\frac{1}{s} - \frac{1}{cs^2} \right) e^{-as} + \frac{q}{cs^2} e^{-(a+c)s}$$

111. Using the results of Prob. 110, determine the deflection of the beam shown in Fig. 69.

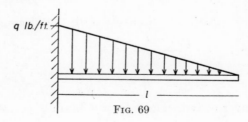

FIG. 69

112. A uniform beam of length l has a concentrated load P at $x = a$. If the left end is clamped and the right end is hinged, both being at the same elevation, determine the deflection.

113. Figure 70 shows a uniform cantilever beam with a narrow slot of width c at $x = a$. Show that the deflection is given by the equation

$$y(x) = -\frac{Pl}{2EI}x^2 + \frac{Px^3}{6EI}$$

$$-\frac{P(l-a)}{EI}\left(\frac{I}{I_c} - 1\right)$$

$$c(x-a)\mathfrak{U}(x-a)$$

where I_c is the moment of inertia at the slot.

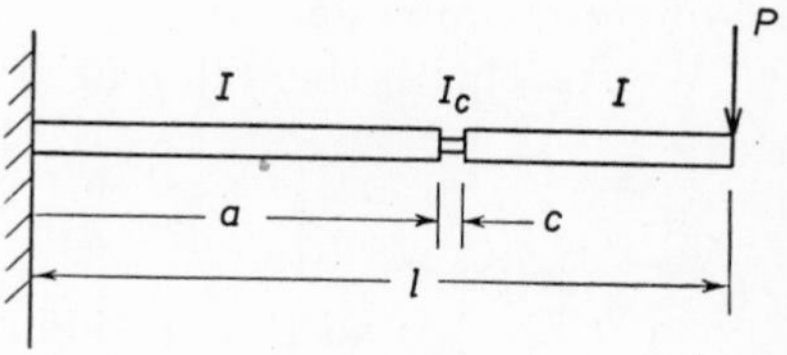

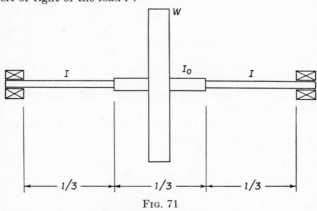

FIG. 70

114. A simply supported beam with a load P at mid-span has a slot of width c at $x = a$. Show that the deflection is

$$y(x) = -\left\{\frac{Pl^2}{16EI} + \frac{M_a}{EIl}\left(\frac{I}{I_c} - 1\right)c(l-a)\right\}x$$

$$+ \frac{P}{6EI}\left\{\frac{x^3}{2} - \left(x - \frac{l}{2}\right)^3\mathfrak{U}\left(x - \frac{l}{2}\right)\right\}$$

$$+ \frac{M_a}{EI}\left(\frac{I}{I_c} - 1\right)c(x-a)\mathfrak{U}(x-a)$$

where $M_a = Pa/2$ or $P(l-a)/2$, depending on whether the slot appears to the left or right of the load P.

FIG. 71

115. A flywheel of weight W is pressed on a shaft which has a larger diameter over the middle third of its length as shown in Fig. 71. Assuming the bearings to be rigid, determine the deflection at mid-span in terms of I, I_0, l, and W.

39. Critical Load of Columns. Figure 72 shows a column with arbitrary end conditions. The column is assumed to be long so that failure tends to take place by lateral instability rather than by direct compression.

We start with the differential equation

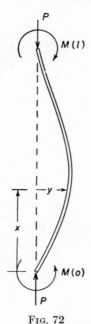

$$\frac{d^2y}{dx^2} = -\left(\frac{P}{EI}\right)y + \frac{M(0)}{EI} \qquad (39.1)$$

and the subsidiary equation becomes

$$\bar{y}(s) = \frac{sy(0) + y'(0) + M(0)/sEI}{s^2 + \beta^2} \qquad (39.2)$$

$$\beta^2 = \frac{P}{EI}$$

Noting that $y(0)$ is zero, we find that the solution in terms of the slope and moment at $x = 0$ is

$$y(x) = \frac{y'(0)}{\beta} \sin \beta x + \frac{M(0)}{EI\beta^2}(1 - \cos \beta x) \qquad (39.3)$$

To evaluate $y'(0)$ and $M(0)$, we note that the deflection, slope, and moment at $x = l$ are

$$y(l) = \frac{y'(0)}{\beta} \sin \beta l + \frac{M(0)}{EI\beta^2}(1 - \cos \beta l) \qquad (39.4)$$

$$y'(l) = y'(0) \cos \beta l + \frac{M(0)}{EI\beta} \sin \beta l \qquad (39.5)$$

FIG. 72

$$M(l) = EIy'(0)\beta \sin \beta l + M(0) \cos \beta l \qquad (39.6)$$

These equations are then sufficient for the evaluation of the critical load for any end conditions.

(a) *Pinned Ends.* In this case $M(0) = M(l) = 0$, and from Eqs. (39.4) and (39.6) we obtain

$$\frac{y'(0)}{\beta} \sin \beta l = 0$$

$$\beta l = \pi$$

$$P_{cr} = \frac{\pi^2 EI}{l^2}$$

(b) *Both Ends Clamped.* The slope at the ends for this case is zero $y'(0) = y'(l) = 0$. From Eqs. (39.4) and (39.6) we obtain

$$(1 - \cos \beta l) = 0$$

and from Eq. (39.5),

$$\sin \beta l = 0$$

Both these equations are satisfied by

$$\beta l = 2\pi$$

$$P_{cr} = \frac{4\pi^2 EI}{l^2}$$

(c) *End $\overset{.}{x} = 0$ Clamped and Other End Pinned and Free.* The boundary conditions for this case are $y'(0) = M(l) = 0$. From Eq. (39.6),

$$\cos \beta l = 0$$

$$\beta l = \frac{\pi}{2}$$

$$P_{cr} = \frac{\pi^2 EI}{4l^2}$$

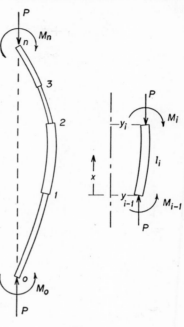

Fig. 73

40. Nonuniform Column. Columns of several sections can be treated operationally by shifting the origin to the end of each section. Thus the differential equation and the subsidiary equation for the ith section from Fig. 73 are

$$E_i I_i \frac{d^2 y}{dx^2} = -P(y - y_{i-1}) + M_{i-1} \tag{40.1}$$

$$\bar{y}(s) = \frac{y_{i-1}}{s} + \frac{y'_{i-1}}{s^2 + \beta_i^2} + \frac{M_{i-1}}{E_i I_i s(s^2 + \beta_i^2)} \tag{40.2}$$

where

$$\beta_i = \sqrt{\frac{P}{E_i I_i}} \tag{40.3}$$

Taking the inverse, we have

$$y(x) = y_{i-1} + \frac{y'_{i-1}}{\beta_i} \sin \beta_i x + \frac{M_{i-1}}{E_i I_i \beta_i^2} (1 - \cos \beta_i x) \tag{40.4}$$

Differentiating and letting $x = l_i$, we obtain the equations for the deflection, slope, and moment at i in terms of corresponding quantities at $i - 1$:

$$y_i = y_{i-1} + \frac{y'_{i-1}}{\beta_i} \sin \beta_i l_i + \frac{M_{i-1}}{E_i I_i \beta_i^2} (1 - \cos \beta_i l_i) \qquad (40.5)$$

$$y'_i = y'_{i-1} \cos \beta_i l_i + \frac{M_{i-1}}{E_i I_i \beta_i} \sin \beta_i l_i \qquad (40.6)$$

$$M_i = -y'_{i-1} E_i I_i \beta_i \sin \beta_i l_i - M_{i-1} \cos \beta_i l_i \qquad (40.7)$$

It is convenient to express these three equations in matrix form as follows:

$$
\begin{bmatrix} y_i \\ y'_i \\ M_i \end{bmatrix} =
\begin{bmatrix}
1 & \dfrac{1}{\beta_i} \sin \beta_i l_i & \dfrac{1}{E_i I_i \beta_i^2} (1 - \cos \beta_i l_i) \\
0 & \cos \beta_i l_i & \dfrac{1}{E_i I_i \beta_i} \sin \beta_i l_i \\
0 & -E_i I_i \beta_i \sin \beta_i l_i & \cos \beta_i l_i
\end{bmatrix}
\begin{bmatrix} y_{i-1} \\ y'_{i-1} \\ M_{i-1} \end{bmatrix} \qquad (40.8)
$$

A similar equation can be obtained for $i - 1$ in terms of $i - 2$, and so on. By repeated multiplication of the matrices, quantities at station n can be expressed in terms of corresponding quantities at station 0 by the equation

$$
\begin{bmatrix} y_n \\ y'_n \\ M_n \end{bmatrix} =
\begin{bmatrix}
A_{11} & A_{12} & A_{13} \\
0 & A_{22} & A_{23} \\
0 & A_{32} & A_{33}
\end{bmatrix}
\begin{bmatrix} y_0 \\ y'_0 \\ M_0 \end{bmatrix} \qquad (40.9)
$$

The equation for the critical load follows by applying the boundary conditions to Eq. (40.9).

(a) *Pin-ended Columns.* The boundary conditions are

$$y_n = y_0 = M_n = M_0 = 0$$

By substitution into Eq. (40.9), the equation for the critical load becomes

$$A_{12} = A_{32} = 0 \qquad (40.10)$$

(b) *Fixed-End Columns.* We have the boundary conditions

$$y_n = y_0 = y'_n = y'_0 = 0$$

The critical load is then given by the equation

$$A_{13} = A_{23} = 0 \qquad (40.11)$$

(c) When only a few sections are involved, simple analytical expressions can be obtained for the critical load. However, for many sections the simplest procedure is to choose a β_n and then compute the elements of the matrix equation for each section. This is possible, since

$$\frac{\beta_{n-1}}{\beta_n} = \sqrt{\frac{E_n I_n}{E_{n-1} I_{n-1}}} \tag{40.12}$$

By plotting A_{12}, A_{32}, . . . , we can obtain the critical load by satisfying the equation corresponding to the particular boundary conditions.

Problems

116. From the equations of Section 40, obtain the equations for the critical load of a uniform column as given in Section 39.

117. Write the boundary equations for a column of several sections if end 0 is fixed and the end n is pinned and free. Show that the critical load is given by the equation

$$A_{33} = 0$$

118. For a pin-ended column of two sections, show that the equation for the critical load is

$$\frac{\tan \beta_2 l_2}{\beta_2} = -\frac{\tan \beta_1 l_1}{\beta_1}$$

119. If a uniform column is fixed at one end and the other end is pinned and guided so that its deflection is zero, write its differential equation and discuss its solution.

References

Thomson, W. T., "Matrix Solution for the n-Section Column," *Journal of the Aeronautical Sciences*, **16,** 10 (October 1949), page 623.

CHAPTER 5
Complex Variable Theory

The elementary treatment of the inversion process given in the first chapter is often found to be inadequate for more advanced problems. In this chapter we shall approach the subject of the operational method in a more general way by means of the theory of complex variables. In fact, it is hardly possible to obtain a thorough understanding of the subject of Laplace transformation without some knowledge of complex-variable theory. To a beginner the theory of complex variables may appear somewhat abstract and remotely related to physical interpretations. However, it is one of the most useful forms of mathematics for the applied mathematical fields. Only those parts of the theory which are essential to Laplace transformation are briefly presented. References at the end of the chapter should be consulted for further details.

41. Complex Variable. If the real and complex parts of a complex quantity are variable, the quantity is called a *complex variable*. For example,

$$z = x + iy \tag{41.1}$$

is a complex variable where x and y are variable.

We now define another complex variable,

$$w = u + iv \tag{41.2}$$

so related to z that for each value of z there corresponds a value of w

$$w = f(z) \tag{41.3}$$

Thus, when the variable z describes a curve in the z-plane, the corresponding values of w will trace out some curve in the w-plane as shown in Fig. 74.

42. Analytic Function. A function of a complex variable which possesses a derivative at every point of a region is said to be *analytic* (or *regular*) over that region. For instance, if $w = 1/z$, the deriva-

90

tive $dw/dz = -1/z^2$ exists for every z except $z = 0$. Thus $w = 1/z$ is analytic except at the origin.

We define the derivative of the function $w = f(z)$ by the equation

$$\frac{dw}{dz} = \lim_{\Delta z \to 0} \frac{\Delta w}{\Delta z} = \lim_{\Delta z \to 0} \frac{f(z + \Delta z) - f(z)}{\Delta z} \tag{42.1}$$

Since $\Delta z = \Delta x + i\,\Delta y$, there are any number of different ways of approaching this limit. Thus for an analytic function, it is necessary to demand that the above limit be independent of the manner

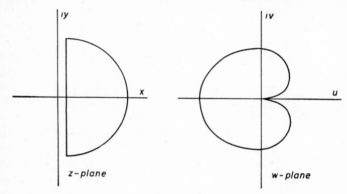

F$_{\text{IG}}$. 74

in which Δz approaches zero. For instance, if Δz is first taken in the x-direction and then in the y-direction, we obtain the following two expressions:

$$\lim_{\Delta z \to 0} \frac{\Delta w}{\Delta z} = \lim_{\Delta x \to 0} \frac{\Delta u + i\,\Delta v}{\Delta x} = \frac{\partial u}{\partial x} + i\,\frac{\partial v}{\partial x} \tag{42.2}$$

$$\lim_{\Delta z \to 0} \frac{\Delta w}{\Delta z} = \lim_{i\Delta y \to 0} \frac{\Delta u + i\,\Delta v}{i\,\Delta y} = \frac{\partial v}{\partial y} - i\,\frac{\partial u}{\partial y} \tag{42.3}$$

For the limit to be unique, the above equations must be equal, or

$$\frac{\partial u}{\partial x} = \frac{\partial v}{\partial y} \tag{42.4}$$

$$\frac{\partial u}{\partial y} = -\frac{\partial v}{\partial x} \tag{42.5}$$

These equations which u and v must satisfy are known as the *Cauchy-Riemann* equations. They are necessary conditions for the existance of the derivative. The Cauchy-Riemann equations can also be shown to be sufficient conditions for the existance of a derivative.* Thus an analytic function must satisfy the Cauchy-Riemann equations. Moreover, if $f(z)$ has a derivative at a given point z_0, it must also be continuous and single-valued at that point. The converse is not necessarily true, however.

It is fortunate that many ordinary functions, such as polynomials and sines, are analytic. For such functions the usual rules of differentiation hold.

EXAMPLE 42.1: Determine whether $w = z^3$ satisfies the Cauchy-Riemann equations.

Writing w in terms of x and y,

$$w = (x + iy)^3 = (x^3 - 3xy^2) + i(3x^2y - y^3)$$

we have
$$u = x^3 - 3xy^2$$
$$v = 3x^2y - y^3$$

The Cauchy-Riemann equations

$$\frac{\partial u}{\partial x} = 3x^2 - 3y^2 = \frac{\partial v}{\partial y}$$

$$\frac{\partial u}{\partial y} = -6xy = -\frac{\partial v}{\partial x}$$

are thus satisfied, and the derivative of the function $w = z^3$ exists and is equal to

$$\frac{dw}{dz} = 3z^2 = 3(x + iy)^2$$

Problems

120. For $w = z^3$ show that

$$\frac{dw}{dz} = \frac{\partial w}{\partial x} = -i\frac{\partial w}{\partial y} = \frac{\partial u}{\partial x} - i\frac{\partial u}{\partial y}$$

121. Determine whether the function $w = \sin z$ satisfies the Cauchy-Riemann equations.

122. Is $w = 2x + iy$ analytic?

123. If the increment Δz is taken in the radial and tangential directions, show that

$$\frac{dw}{dz} = \left(\frac{\partial u}{\partial r} + i\frac{\partial v}{\partial r}\right)e^{i\theta} = \frac{1}{r}\left(\frac{\partial v}{\partial \theta} - i\frac{\partial u}{\partial \theta}\right)e^{-i\theta}$$

where
$$w = f(z) \quad \text{and} \quad z = r\,e^{i\theta}$$

* See references at end of chapter—Churchill, page 30, and Osgood, page 35.

43. Singularities. Points where the function ceases to be analytic are called *singularities*. For single-valued functions, there are two kinds of singularities as follows:

(a) *Poles* (*Unessential Singularities*). Poles are points where the function becomes infinite to a finite order; that is, the singularity can always be removed by multiplying the function by a suitable factor of finite index. As an example, the function

$$f(z) = \frac{z}{(z-a)^n}$$

for n a finite integer has a pole of order n at $z = a$, which can be removed by multiplying the function by $(z-a)^n$. Thus

$$\lim_{z \to a} (z-a)^n f(z) \neq \infty$$

(b) *Essential Singularity* (*Pole of Infinite Order*). For an essential singularity, the limit

$$\lim_{z \to a} (z-a)^n f(z)$$

does not exist for a finite value of n. For example,

$$e^{\frac{1}{z}} = 1 + \frac{1}{z} + \frac{1}{2!z^2} + \frac{1}{3!z^3} + \cdots$$

has an essential singularity at $z = 0$. Another example is an expansion of the form

$$f(z) = \sum_{n=0}^{-\infty} (z-a)^n$$

which has an essential singularity at $z = a$.

44. Branch Points. If $w = f(s)$ is a single-valued function, each point of the z-plane corresponds to one point of the w-plane. For a multivalued function, each point of the z-plane may correspond to more than one point of the w-plane.

Consider, for example, the function $w = z^{\frac{1}{2}}$ taken over the circular path of Fig. 75(a). Changing to polar form,

$$z = r\,e^{i\theta}$$
$$w = r^{\frac{1}{2}}\,e^{i\theta/2}$$

we find that in completing one circuit of 0 to 2π radians in the z-plane the corresponding values in the w-plane cover 0 to π radians, as shown in Fig. 75(b). Continuing around the z-plane for the second time, 2π to 4π radians, w describes the angle π to 2π radians (indicated by a broken line in the w-plane). Hence a point such as b in the z-plane corresponds to two points b_1 and b_2 in the w-plane.

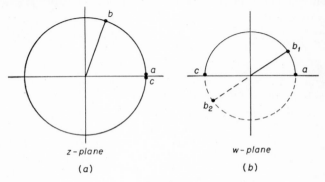

z - plane   w - plane

(a)   (b)

Fig. 75

The two regions of the w-plane—0 to π, π to 2π—are referred to as the two *branches* of the function $w = z^{\frac{1}{2}}$. The point $z = 0$ separating the two branch values b_1 and b_2 is called the *branch point*.

Consider again the same function $w = z^{\frac{1}{2}}$ taken over the contour of Fig. 76 and not enclosing the branch point. In the process of

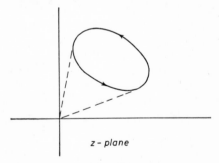

z - plane

Fig. 76

going around this curve, the argument of z merely oscillates between the two extreme values shown, and hence $w = z^{\frac{1}{2}}$ is single-valued over such a curve. Values acquired by multivalued function, then, generally depend on the path described.

Multivalued functions restricted to a single branch are single-valued. Generally the first or *principal branch* is considered; and if a contour encloses a branch point, the argument in the z-plane is restricted to 2π radians by means of a barrier or *branch cut* as shown in Fig. 77.

A branch point is generally considered to be a singularity, since its inclusion within the closed contour results in multiple values of w which fail to comply with the requirements of an analytic

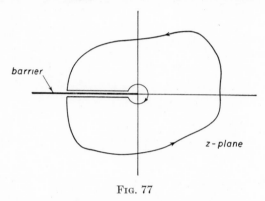

barrier

z - plane

FIG. 77

function. Other multivalued functions possessing this peculiarity are

$$w = \ln z = \ln |z| + i\theta$$
$$w = \sin^{-1} z$$
$$w = (z - a)^{1/n} \qquad (n = \text{a finite integer})$$
$$w = e^{\sqrt{z}}$$

45. Cauchy-Goursat Theorem. The Cauchy-Goursat theorem states that if a function $f(z)$ is analytic within and upon a closed contour, the line integral taken around the contour is zero.

$$\oint f(z) \, dz = 0 \qquad (45.1)$$

The notation $\oint$ is used to denote an integration around a closed curve; the arrow indicates that the integration is to proceed in the counterclockwise direction.

To prove this theorem, let the curve C of Fig. 78 be the specified contour around which $w = f(z)$ is to be integrated. By dividing the region within C into a series of rectangles, we can concentrate our attention on one of them. If we consider the integration around this rectangle to be the product of the average value of w of

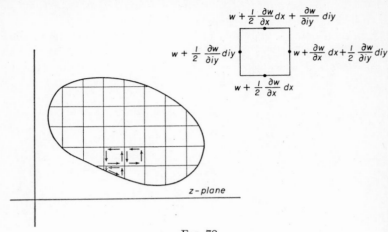

FIG. 78

each side and its length, we obtain

$$\left(w + \frac{\partial w}{\partial x}\frac{dx}{2}\right)dx + \left(w + \frac{\partial w}{\partial x}dx + \frac{\partial w}{\partial iy}\frac{diy}{2}\right)diy$$

$$+ \left(w + \frac{\partial w}{\partial x}\frac{dx}{2} + \frac{\partial w}{i\,\partial y}i\,dy\right)(-dx) + \left(w + \frac{\partial w}{i\,\partial y}\frac{i\,dy}{2}\right)(-i\,dy)$$

$$= \left(\frac{\partial w}{\partial x} - \frac{\partial w}{i\,\partial y}\right)i\,dx\,dy \quad (45.2)$$

Substituting $w = u + iv$ in this result, we obtain the equation

$$\frac{\partial w}{\partial x} - \frac{\partial w}{i\,\partial y} = \left(\frac{\partial u}{\partial x} - \frac{\partial v}{\partial y}\right) + i\left(\frac{\partial v}{\partial x} + \frac{\partial u}{\partial y}\right). \quad (45.3)$$

Since the function is analytic, the right side of this equation, which corresponds to the Cauchy-Riemann equation, is zero, and hence the integration around each of these rectangles is zero.

We note next that in integrating around adjoining rectangles, each side is traversed in opposite directions, the net result being equivalent to integrating around the outer curve C. We therefore arrive at the result

$$\oint f(z)\,dz = 0$$

when the function $w = f(z)$ is analytic within and on the closed contour C.

As a consequence of the Cauchy-Goursat theorem, we can state that if $f(z)$ is analytic in a given region, the line integral between two points in this region is independent of the path taken.   Refer-

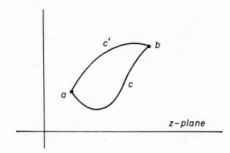

Fig. 79

ring to Fig. 79, the integral around the curve $acbc'a$ is zero, and hence the integral along the curve acb must be the negative of the integral along $bc'a$.   Thus the integral from a to b is independent of the path.

EXAMPLE 45.1: The function $w = z$ is analytic for all finite values of z.   Show that its integral around the two contours shown in Fig. 80(a) and (b) is zero.

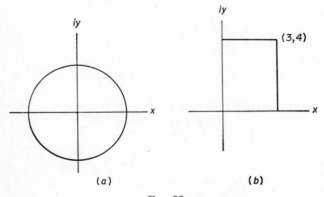

Fig. 80

(a) For the circular path, we let

$$z = r\,e^{i\theta}$$
$$dz = ir\,e^{i\theta}\,d\theta$$

and the integral becomes

$$\oint z\,dz = ir^2 \int_0^{2\pi} e^{i2\theta}\,d\theta = \frac{r^2}{2}\,e^{2i\theta}\Big]_0^{2\pi} = 0$$

(b) For the rectangular path, we break up the integral along each side as follows:

$$\oint z\,dz = \int_0^3 x\,dx + \int_0^4 (3 + iy)i\,dy + \int_3^0 (x + i4)\,dx + \int_4^0 (iy)i\,dy$$

$$= \frac{x^2}{2}\Big]_0^3 + \left(3iy - \frac{y^2}{2}\right)\Big]_0^4 + \left(\frac{x^2}{2} + i4x\right)\Big]_3^0 - \frac{y^2}{2}\Big]_4^0 = 0$$

The integral $\oint z\,dz$ is therefore zero for both curves, as stated by the Cauchy-Goursat theorem.

EXAMPLE 45.2: The function $w = 1/z$ has a simple pole at the origin but is analytic everywhere else. Show that its integral around a circular path enclosing the origin is equal to $2\pi i$.

We let
$$z = r\,e^{i\theta}$$
$$dz = ir\,e^{i\theta}\,d\theta$$

and the integral becomes

$$\oint \frac{dz}{z} = i \int_0^{2\pi} d\theta = 2\pi i$$

EXAMPLE 45.3: The function $w = 1/(z - a)$ is analytic except at the pole $z = a$. Show that the integral around a circle with center $z = 0$ is zero if a lies outside the circle and is $2\pi i$ if a is enclosed.

If we make the substitution $z - a = \lambda$,

$$\oint \frac{dz}{z - a} = \oint \frac{d\lambda}{\lambda} = \ln|\lambda| + i\theta$$

In going around a closed path, $|\lambda|$ returns to its original value so that $\ln|\lambda| = 0$. If a is outside the closed curve, the angle θ returns to its original value, and hence the result is zero. If a is enclosed,

$\theta = 2\pi - 0.$ Thus

$$\oint \frac{dz}{z - a} = \begin{cases} 0 & (a \text{ not enclosed}) \\ 2\pi i & (a \text{ enclosed}) \end{cases}$$

The two cases are illustrated in Fig. 81.

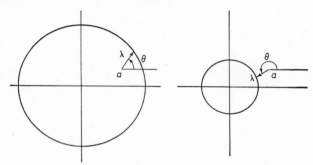

FIG. 81

Problems

124. Evaluate the integral

$$\int_0^{1+i} x \, dz$$

along the straight-line path from 0 to $1 + i$, and along the path corresponding to the x and y projections.

125. Evaluate $\oint (x - y) \, dz$ around a circle of unit radius with center at the origin.

126. Evaluate $\oint dz/z^2$ around a circle with center at the origin. *Hint:* Let $z = r \, e^{i\theta} = r(\cos \theta + i \sin \theta)$

127. Prove that

$$\oint \frac{dz}{(z - a)^n} = \begin{cases} 0 & (\text{for } n \text{ an integer not } 1) \\ 2\pi i & (\text{for } n = 1) \end{cases}$$

128. Show that the following integrals are zero around a circle of radius 1 and center $z = 0$.

(a) $\oint \dfrac{dz}{z - 3}$,

(b) $\oint \dfrac{z \, dz}{\cos z}$,

(c) $\oint \dfrac{e^z \, dz}{z - 2}$

(d) $\oint e^{-z} \, dz$

46. Integral Expression of an Analytic Function.   Let $f(z)$ be analytic on and within the contour C shown in Fig. 82, and let a be a point within.   We now define a new function:

$$g = \frac{f(z)}{(z-a)} \qquad (46.1)$$

with a singularity at a.   If we draw a small circle around a, $g(z)$ will be analytic in the area bounded by C and the circle, and the integra-

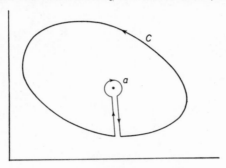

FIG. 82

tion around the path shown by the arrows will be zero.

$$\oint_C \frac{f(z)}{z-a}\, dz - \int \frac{f(z)}{(z-a)}\, dz = 0 \qquad (46.2)$$

Since $f(z)$ is analytic at a, we can let its value on the small circle be

$$f(z) \cong f(a) + \epsilon \qquad (46.3)$$

where ϵ is a small quantity.   Substituting into Eq. (46.2), we obtain

$$\oint_C \frac{f(z)\, dz}{(z-a)} = f(a) \int_a \frac{dz}{(z-a)} + \int_a \frac{\epsilon\, dz}{(z-a)} \qquad (46\ 4)$$

If r is the radius of the small circle, $(z-a)$ on the circumference is

$$(z-a) = r\, e^{i\theta}$$
$$dz = ir\, e^{i\theta}\, d\theta$$

and Eq. (46.4) becomes

$$\oint_C \frac{f(z)\, dz}{(z-a)} = f(a)2\pi i + i \int_0^{2\pi} \epsilon\, dz \qquad (46.5)$$

We can now reduce the radius of the small circle so that $\epsilon \to 0$. Thus

$$f(a) = \frac{1}{2\pi i} \oint_C \frac{f(z)\, dz}{(z - a)} \tag{46.6}$$

and the function $f(z)$ at a is expressed by a contour integral around a path enclosing a.

This equation, which is known as *Cauchy's integral formula*, states that if we know the values of an analytic function at the boundary, we also know the value of the function at any point within the boundary. The equation suggests several physical interpretations. For instance, the temperature at any point within a body is dependent on the temperature distribution on the boundary surface. The deflection of a membrane stretched across a closed loop of wire depends on the shape of the wire and its elevation.

EXAMPLE 46.1: Using Eq. (46.6), show that

$$\oint \frac{dz}{z - a} = 2\pi i$$

for any point within a closed contour. We have for this case $f(z) = 1$; consequently, $f(a) = 1$, and the above equation is proved.

EXAMPLE 46.2: The function $f(z) = z^2$ is equal to a^2 at $z = a$. Verify this statement by evaluating the integral of Eq. (46.6) with $f(z) = z^2$.

Let $(z - a) = \lambda$; then

$$f(a) = \frac{1}{2\pi i} \oint \frac{z^2\, dz}{z - a} = \frac{1}{2\pi i} \oint \frac{(\lambda + a)^2\, d\lambda}{\lambda}$$

$$= \frac{1}{2\pi i} \oint \left(\lambda + 2a + \frac{a^2}{\lambda} \right) d\lambda$$

The first two terms of the integrand are analytic, and hence their integrals are zero. Thus

$$f(a) = \frac{1}{2\pi i} \oint \frac{z^2\, dz}{z - a} = \frac{a^2}{2\pi i} \oint \frac{d\lambda}{\lambda} = a^2$$

EXAMPLE 46.3: Show by means of Eq. (46.6) that if a function is analytic, all its derivatives exist.

If we let $a = z$ and $z = s$, Eq. (46.6) becomes

$$f(z) = \frac{1}{2\pi i} \oint \frac{f(s)\, ds}{(s - z)}$$

where z becomes a fixed point and s now varies along the enclosing curve C. Differentiating with respect to z, we have

$$f'(z) = \frac{1}{2\pi i} \oint \frac{f(s)\, ds}{(s - z)^2}$$

$$f''(z) = \frac{2!}{2\pi i} \oint \frac{f(s)\, ds}{(s - z)^3}$$

$$f^{(n)}(z) = \frac{n!}{2\pi i} \oint \frac{f(s)\, ds}{(s - z)^{n+1}}$$

Thus, if $f(z)$ is analytic, all its derivatives exist.

EXAMPLE 46.4: By means of Cauchy's integral formula, show that

$$\frac{1}{2\pi i} \int \frac{ds}{(s - a)^n} = \begin{cases} 0 & (n \neq 1) \\ 1 & (n = 1) \end{cases}$$

Let $f(s) = 1$; then $f'(s) = f''(s) = \cdots = 0$. Thus the above relationship is obtained.

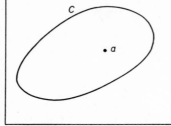

FIG. 83

47. Theory of Residues.
In Fig. 83, let $f(z)$ be analytic on and within the closed contour C except at $z = a$, where there is a pole of order n. Then

$$f(z) = \frac{f(z)(z - a)^n}{(z - a)^n} = \frac{F(z)}{(z - a)^n} \tag{47.1}$$

where $F(z)$ is analytic on and within the closed contour, including the point a. Since $F(z)$ is analytic at a, we can expand $F(z)$ about a by the Taylor series:

$$F(z) = F(a) + F'(a)(z - a) + \frac{F''(a)}{2!}(z - a)^2$$

$$+ \cdots \frac{F^{(n)}(a)}{n!}(z - a)^n + \cdots \tag{47.2}$$

where all the derivatives $F^{(n)}(a)$ exist according to Example 46.3.

Substituting Eq. (47.2) into (47.1), we obtain the series

$$f(z) = \frac{F(a)}{(z-a)^n} + \frac{F'(a)}{(z-a)^{n-1}} + \frac{F''(a)}{2!(z-a)^{n-2}} + \cdots$$
$$+ \frac{F^{(n-1)}(a)}{(n-1)!(z-a)} + \frac{F^{(n)}(a)}{n!} + \frac{F^{(n+1)}(a)}{(n+1)!}(z-a) + \cdots \qquad (47.3)$$

which is referred to as the *Laurent expansion*. We now consider the integral

$$\frac{1}{2\pi i} \oint f(z)\,dz = \frac{F(a)}{2\pi i} \oint \frac{dz}{(z-a)^n} + \frac{F''(a)}{2\pi i} \oint \frac{dz}{(z-a)^{n-1}} + \cdots$$
$$+ \frac{F^{(n-1)}(a)}{(n-1)!2\pi i} \oint \frac{dz}{(z-a)} + \frac{F^{(n)}(a)}{n!2\pi i} \oint dz + \cdots$$
$$+ \frac{F^{(n+1)}(a)}{(n+1)!2\pi i} \oint (z-a)\,dz + \cdots \frac{F^{(n+m)}(a)}{(n+m)!2\pi i} \oint (z-a)^m\,dz$$
$$+ \cdots \qquad (47.4)$$

In the above equation, all integrals on the right side with the exception of one are zero. For instance,

$$\oint (z-a)^n\,dz = 0 \quad (n = 0, 1, 2, 3, \cdots)$$

since the function is analytic. The second type (see Example 46.4) has the value

$$\int \frac{dz}{(z-a)^n} = \begin{cases} 0 & \text{(for } n \neq 1) \\ 2\pi i & \text{(for } n = 1) \end{cases}$$

Consequently, Eq. (47.4) reduces to

$$\frac{1}{2\pi i} \oint f(z)\,dz = \frac{F^{(n-1)}(a)}{(n-1)!} = \Re^{(n)} \qquad (47.5)$$

The right side of this equation is the coefficient of the $(z-a)^{-1}$ term of the Laurent expansion given by Eq. (47.3). It is the only coefficient of the Laurent expansion which affects the value of the integral of $f(z)$ around a closed contour C, and is called the *residue* $\Re^{(n)}$ of $f(z)$.

If there is more than one pole on or within the contour C, we can deform the path of integration as shown in Fig. 84 and apply the results just obtained. The deformed contour C' now excludes all the poles, and so we can write

$$\frac{1}{2\pi i}\oint f(z)\,dz = 0 = \frac{1}{2\pi i}\oint_C f(z)\,dz - \frac{1}{2\pi i}\oint_{C_1} f(z)\,dz$$

$$-\frac{1}{2\pi i}\oint_{C_2} f(z)\,dz - \cdots \quad (47.6)$$

Thus the integral around the outer curve C is

$$\frac{1}{2\pi i}\oint_C f(z)\,dz = \Re_1 + \Re_2 + \cdots = \sum \Re \quad (47.7)$$

We conclude from this equation that if $f(z)$ is analytic except for singularities at the poles, the integral around the closed path is

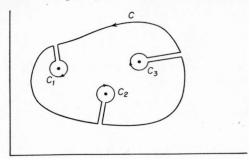

FIG. 84

equal to the sum of the residues of the poles. From Eqs. (47.5) and (47.1), the residue for the nth order pole is

$$\Re^{(n)} = \frac{F^{(n-1)}(a)}{(n-1)!} = \lim_{z \to a} \frac{d^{n-1}}{dz^{n-1}} \frac{f(z)(z-a)^n}{(n-1)!} \quad (47.8)$$

which states that the function $f(z)$ is first multiplied by $(z-a)^n/(n-1)!$, differentiated with respect to z, $(n-1)$ times, after which we let $z = a$. For the simple pole, this reduces to

$$\Re = \lim_{z \to a} f(z)(z-a) \quad (47.9)$$

since $0! = 1$; that is, $(n-1)! = n!/n = 1$ if $n = 1$.

In some cases the denominator of $f(z)$ is not readily factorable, in which case we proceed as follows. Let $f(z) = A(z)/B(z)$ contain only simple poles a_k.   Then from Eq. (47.9) we can write

$$\sum \mathfrak{R} = \sum_{k=1}^{n} \lim_{z \to a_k} (z - a_k) \frac{A(z)}{B(z)} \tag{47.10}$$

where a_k are the roots of $B(z) = 0$.   We note here that we have an indeterminate form $\frac{0}{0}$, and hence by L'Hospital's rule we obtain

$$\sum \mathfrak{R} = \sum_{k=1}^{n} \lim_{z \to a_k} \frac{(z - a_k)A'(z) + A(z)}{B'(z)} = \sum_{k=1}^{n} \frac{A(a_k)}{B'(a_k)} \tag{47.11}$$

Sometimes it is simpler to determine the residues by expansion of $f(z)$ into a Laurent series, particularly when $f(z)$ contains multiple-order poles.

EXAMPLE 47.1: Evaluate the integral

$$\int \frac{z^2 \, dz}{z + 1}$$

by the residue theorem.

The function in this case is

$$f(z) = \frac{z^2}{z + 1}$$

which has a simple pole at $z = -1$.   From Eq. (47.9), the residue at $z = -1$ is

$$\lim_{z \to -1} (z + 1) \frac{z^2}{(z + 1)} = 1$$

and the integral around any closed path enclosing the point $z = -1$ is

$$\int \frac{z^2 \, dz}{z + 1} = 2\pi i$$

We can arrive at the same result by expanding $z^2/(z + 1)$ into a Laurent series about the pole $z = -1$.   Letting $z + 1 = \lambda$, $z^2 = (\lambda - 1)^2$, and $dz = d\lambda$, we shift our pole to $\lambda = 0$.   Thus

$$\frac{z^2}{z + 1} = \frac{(\lambda - 1)^2}{\lambda} = \lambda - 2 + \frac{1}{\lambda}$$

The residue is then the coefficient of $1/\lambda$, or 1, and we arrive at the value of $2\pi i$ for its integral.

EXAMPLE 47.2: Evaluate the integral

$$\oint \frac{dz}{(z-a)^2}$$

where the integration is carried over a closed path enclosing the point $z = a$.

The function $f(z) = 1/(z-a)^2$ has a pole of order 2 at $z = a$ and the residue from Eq. (47.8) is

$$\lim_{z \to a} \frac{d}{dz} \frac{(z-a)^2}{(2-1)!} \frac{1}{(z-a)^2} = 0$$

Thus the integral is zero:

$$\oint \frac{dz}{(z-a)^2} = 0$$

This result could have been established by inspection, since $1/(z-a)^2$ can be considered to be one term of the Laurent expansion with all other coefficients equal to zero. The residue, being the coefficient of $1/(z-a)$, is necessarily zero for this case.

EXAMPLE 47.3: Determine the residue of $f(z) = e^{iz}/(z^2 + a^2)$, and specify the integration path.

The poles are $z = \pm ia$, which are conjugate points on the imaginary axis. From Eq. (47.9), the residues are

$$\sum \Re = \lim_{z \to -ia} \frac{e^{iz}}{(z-ia)} + \lim_{z \to ia} \frac{e^{iz}}{(z+ia)}$$

$$= -\frac{e^a}{2ia} + \frac{e^{-a}}{2ia} = \frac{i}{a}\left(\frac{e^a - e^{-a}}{2}\right) = \frac{i}{a} \sinh a$$

Consequently, the integral around any closed contour enclosing the poles $z = \pm ia$ is

$$\oint \frac{e^{iz}\, dz}{z^2 + a^2} = \frac{2\pi i^2}{a} \sinh a = -\frac{2\pi}{a} \sinh a$$

EXAMPLE 47.4: Evaluate the integral

$$\oint \frac{z\, dz}{\sin nz}$$

around a circle of radius $|z| < \pi/n$ with center at the origin.

The function $z/\sin nz$ has no pole at the origin, since

$$\lim_{z \to 0} \frac{z}{\sin nz} = \frac{1}{n}$$

The closest singularity is at $z = \pi/n$. Hence the integral around the circle with center $z = 0$, and radius $|z| < \pi/n$ is zero.

Problems

129. Expand the function

$$f(z) = \frac{1}{z(z-1)}$$

into a Laurent series (a) about $z = 0$ and (b) about $z = 1$, and determine the residues at the poles. (c) If $f(z)$ is integrated around a closed path enclosing the origin and cutting the x-axis between 0 and 1, determine its value.

130. Expand the function $f(z) = e^z/z^2$ into a Laurent series and determine its residue. Determine its integral around any circular contour with center at $z = 0$.

131. Evaluate the integral

$$\oint_C \frac{e^z \, dz}{\sin nz}$$

where (a) C is a circle with center at $z = 0$ and radius $|z| < \pi/n$, (b) radius is specified as $\pi/n < |z| < 2\pi/n$.

132. Determine the sum of the residues of the following functions:

(a) $f(z) = \dfrac{z}{z^2 + z - 6}$

(b) $f(z) = \dfrac{1}{z(z + a)}$

(c) $f(z) = \dfrac{1}{z^2 + 1}$

(d) $f(z) = \dfrac{e^z}{(z - a)^3}$

133. Evaluate the integral

$$\oint \frac{e^z \, dz}{\cos nz}$$

around a circle of radius $|z| = 1/n$ and center $z = 0$.

134. Evaluate the integral

$$\oint \frac{dz}{z \cos z}$$

around a unit circle.

135. Determine the poles of

$$f(z) = \frac{\sinh z}{z \cosh z}$$

and find the sum of the residues.

136. Show that the residue of

$$f(z) = \frac{e^{zt}}{z \sin nz}$$

at the origin is t/n. Specify a contour C which will result in the value

$$\oint_C \frac{e^{zt}\, dz}{z \sin nz} = 2\pi i \frac{t}{n}$$

48. Complex Form of the Fourier Series. If a function $f(t)$ is periodic with a period τ, then $f(t) = f(t + \tau)$. Such functions can be represented by a Fourier series, provided the function is finite and contains only a finite number of discontinuities. The series and the coefficients are

$$f(t) = \sum_{n=1}^{\infty} a_n \sin n\omega t + \sum_{n=0}^{\infty} b_n \cos n\omega t \qquad (48.1)$$

$$\left. \begin{array}{l} a_n = \dfrac{2}{\tau} \displaystyle\int_{-\tau/2}^{+\tau/2} f(t) \sin n\omega t\, dt \\[2mm] b_n = \dfrac{2}{\tau} \displaystyle\int_{-\tau/2}^{+\tau/2} f(t) \cos n\omega t\, dt \\[2mm] b_0 = \dfrac{1}{\tau} \displaystyle\int_{-\tau/2}^{+\tau/2} f(t)\, dt \end{array} \right\} \qquad (48.2)$$

We now convert these equations to a complex form by means of the substitution

$$\sin n\omega t = \frac{1}{2i}\left(e^{in\omega t} - e^{-in\omega t}\right)$$

$$\cos n\omega t = \tfrac{1}{2}\left(e^{in\omega t} + e^{-in\omega t}\right)$$

Hence

$$f(t) = \frac{1}{2i}\sum_{n=0}^{\infty}(a_n + ib_n)e^{in\omega t} - \frac{1}{2i}\sum_{n=0}^{\infty}(a_n - ib_n)e^{-in\omega t} \qquad (48.3)$$

Noting that

$$\frac{1}{2i} (a_n + ib_n) = \frac{1}{\tau} \int_{-\tau/2}^{+\tau/2} f(t) \, e^{-in\omega t} \, dt$$

$$\frac{1}{2i} (a_n - ib_n) = \frac{-1}{\tau} \int_{-\tau/2}^{+\tau/2} f(t) \, e^{in\omega t} \, dt$$

we find that Eq. (48.3) becomes

$$f(t) = \sum_{n=0}^{\infty} \frac{e^{in\omega t}}{\tau} \int_{-\tau/2}^{+\tau/2} f(t) \, e^{-in\omega t} \, dt + \sum_{n=0}^{\infty} \frac{e^{-in\omega t}}{\tau} \int_{-\tau/2}^{+\tau/2} f(t) \, e^{in\omega t} \, dt$$

$$(48.4)$$

The expression is unaltered if we change the sign of n in the last term as well as in the summation. Hence the complex form of the Fourier series becomes

$$f(t) = \sum_{n=-\infty}^{+\infty} \frac{e^{in\omega t}}{\tau} \int_{-\tau/2}^{+\tau/2} f(t) \, e^{-in\omega t} \, dt \qquad (48.5)$$

49. The Fourier Integral. Starting with Eq. (48.5) for periodic functions and extending the period to infinity, the function $f(t)$ may include nonperiodic functions.

$$f(t) = \lim_{\tau \to \infty} \sum_{n=-\infty}^{+\infty} \frac{e^{i\frac{2\pi n}{\tau} t}}{\tau} \int_{-\tau/2}^{+\tau/2} f(t) \, e^{-i\frac{2\pi n}{\tau} t} \, dt \qquad (49.1)$$

Letting $\lambda = 2\pi n/\tau$, and remembering that $\tau \to \infty$ and that n is an integer, we find that the differential for the summation with respect to n is

$$d\lambda = \frac{2\pi}{\tau} (n_{k+1} - n_k) = \frac{2\pi}{\tau} \qquad (49.2)$$

Thus the limit is expressible by the Fourier integral

$$f(t) = \frac{1}{2\pi} \int_{-\infty}^{+\infty} e^{i\lambda t} \int_{-\infty}^{+\infty} e^{-i\lambda t} f(t) \, dt \, d\lambda \qquad (49.3)$$

This integral is often expressed by the Fourier transform pair

$$f(\lambda) = \int_{-\infty}^{+\infty} e^{-i\lambda t} f(t)\, dt \left.\begin{matrix} \\ \\ \\ \end{matrix}\right\} \tag{49.4}$$

$$f(t) = \frac{1}{2\pi} \int_{-\infty}^{+\infty} e^{i\lambda t} f(\lambda)\, d\lambda$$

The latter expression for $f(t)$ has the following physical interpretation. $e^{i\lambda t} f(\lambda)\, d\lambda$ is a harmonic function of frequency λ and amplitude $f(\lambda)\, d\lambda$. Thus $f(t)$ is expressed as the infinite sum of harmonic oscillations in which all frequencies from $-\infty$ to $+\infty$ are represented.

50. The Fourier–Mellin Inversion Integral. The function $f(t)$ in the Fourier integral is assumed to exist for $t < 0$. In physical problems we are interested only in the solution for $t > 0$, and thus $f(t)$ can be assumed to be zero for $t < 0$. For such functions, the Fourier integral becomes

$$f(t) = \frac{1}{2\pi} \int_{-\infty}^{+\infty} e^{i\lambda t} \int_{0}^{\infty} e^{-i\lambda t} f(t)\, dt\, d\lambda \tag{50.1}$$

We shall now show the equivalence of Eq. (50.1) to the Fourier–Mellin inversion integral

$$f(t) = \frac{1}{2\pi i} \int_{\gamma-i\infty}^{\gamma+i\infty} e^{st} \bar{f}(s)\, ds \tag{50.2}$$

where $\bar{f}(s)$ is the Laplace transform of $f(t)$ and γ is a positive constant.

Rewriting the right side of Eq. (50.2) as

$$\lim_{\beta \to \infty} \frac{1}{2\pi i} \int_{\gamma-i\beta}^{\gamma+i\beta} e^{st} \int_{0}^{\infty} e^{-st} f(t)\, dt\, ds \tag{50.3}$$

we introduce the following substitutions:

$$s = \gamma + i\lambda$$
$$ds = i\, d\lambda$$
$$\lambda = i(\gamma - s)$$

noting that the limits of s which are $\gamma \pm i\beta$ must be changed to the limits of $\lambda = i[\gamma - (\gamma \pm i\beta)] = \pm\beta$. Thus Eq. (50.3) becomes

$$\lim_{\beta \to \infty} \frac{1}{2\pi i} \int_{-\beta}^{+\beta} e^{(\gamma+i\lambda)t} \int_{0}^{\infty} e^{-(\gamma+i\lambda)t} f(t) \, dt \, i \, d\lambda$$

$$= \frac{e^{\gamma t}}{2\pi} \int_{-\infty}^{+\infty} e^{i\lambda t} \int_{0}^{\infty} e^{-i\lambda t}[e^{-\gamma t}f(t)] \, dt \, d\lambda$$

$$= e^{\gamma t}[e^{-\gamma t} f(t)] = f(t)$$

which verifies the equivalence of the two equations.

Equation (50.2) can be written together with its pair:

$$f(t) = \frac{1}{2\pi i} \int_{\gamma-i\infty}^{\gamma+i\infty} e^{st} \bar{f}(s) \, ds \tag{50.4}$$

$$\bar{f}(s) = \int_{0}^{\infty} e^{-st} f(t) \, dt \tag{50.5}$$

Thus Eq. (50.4) is the inversion of Eq. (50.5). These two equations form the basis for the modern operational calculus. We shall be concerned mainly with Eq. (50.4) as a means of evaluating the inverse transformation of $\bar{f}(s)$. The path $\gamma - i\infty$ to $\gamma + i\infty$, which is a straight line parallel to the imaginary axis, is known as the first *Bromwich path*, sometimes abbreviated by the letters Br₁.

51. Evaluation of the Inversion Integral. The limits of the inversion integral,

$$f(t) = \frac{1}{2\pi i} \int_{\gamma-i\infty}^{\gamma+i\infty} e^{st} \bar{f}(s) \, ds \tag{51.1}$$

signify that the integration is to be performed along a straight line $x = \gamma$ from $-i\infty$ to $+i\infty$. We shall assume now that $\bar{f}(s)$ is analytic and that all the poles lie to the left of line $x = \gamma$. This condition is generally fulfilled for all physical problems possessing stability, since poles to the right of the imaginary axis indicate instability.

Consider now the contour shown in Fig. 85, where the radius R of the circle is chosen large enough to enclose all the poles. The integral along the closed path is then represented as the sum along the two segments

$$\oint = \uparrow\!\int + \ ^\smallfrown\!\!\int \tag{51.2}$$

which is rearranged as follows:

$$\uparrow\!\int = \oint - \ ^\smallfrown\!\!\int \tag{51.3}$$

If we let $R \to \infty$, the integral on the left becomes our inversion integral, which is

$$\int_{\gamma - i\infty}^{\gamma + i\infty} = \oint_{R \to \infty} - \left(\int_{R \to \infty} \right. \tag{51.4}$$

now expressed in terms of a contour integral enclosing all the poles and an integral along a semicircle of infinite radius. *Jordan's lemma** shows that the integral along the semicircle of infinite radius is zero; consequently, from the theory of residues, the right

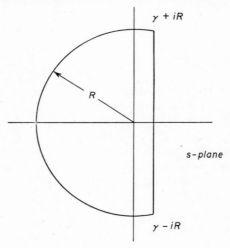

Fig. 85

side of Eq. (51.4) is equal to the sum of the residues of the poles enclosed by the contour integral.

$$f(t) = \frac{1}{2\pi i} \int_{\gamma - i\infty}^{\gamma + i\infty} e^{st} \bar{f}(s) \, ds = \frac{1}{2\pi i} \oint_{R \to \infty} e^{st} \bar{f}(s) \, ds = \sum \Re \tag{51.5}$$

Thus the inverse transformation of $\bar{f}(s)$ is determined as the sum of the residues of $e^{st} \bar{f}(s)$.

52. Inversion by Contour Integration. We shall illustrate here how the inverse transformation is carried out by contour integration.

EXAMPLE 52.1: Evaluate

$$f(t) = \frac{1}{2\pi i} \int_{\gamma - i\infty}^{\gamma + i\infty} \frac{e^{st} \, ds}{s^2(s + a)}$$

* See Appendix B.

The residue at the double pole $s^2 = 0$ is

$$\left\{\frac{d}{ds}\frac{e^{st}}{(s+a)}\right\}_{s=0} = \left\{\frac{(s+a)t\,e^{st} - e^{st}}{(s+a)^2}\right\}_{s=0} = \frac{at-1}{a^2}$$

The residue at $s = -a$ is

$$\left\{\frac{e^{st}}{s^2}\right\}_{s=-a} = \frac{e^{-at}}{a^2}$$

Adding, we find that the inverse transformation is given by the equation

$$f(t) = \mathcal{L}^{-1}\frac{1}{s^2(s+a)} = \frac{1}{a^2}\left(e^{-at} + at - 1\right)$$

EXAMPLE 52.2: Evaluate

$$f(t) = \int_{\gamma-i\infty}^{\gamma+i\infty}\frac{e^{st}\,ds}{s^2(s^2+\omega^2)}$$

The residue at the double pole $s^2 = 0$ is

$$\left\{\frac{d}{ds}\frac{e^{st}}{s^2+\omega^2}\right\}_{s=0} = \left\{\frac{(s^2+\omega^2)t\,e^{st} - 2s\,e^{st}}{(s^2+\omega^2)^2}\right\}_{s=0} = \frac{t}{\omega^2}$$

The residue at $s = \pm i\omega$ is

$$\left\{\frac{e^{st}}{s^2(s+i\omega)}\right\}_{s=i\omega} + \left\{\frac{e^{st}}{s^2(s-i\omega)}\right\}_{s=-i\omega} = -\frac{\sin\omega t}{\omega^3}$$

Therefore $f(t) = \mathcal{L}^{-1}\dfrac{1}{s^2(s^2+\omega^2)} = \dfrac{1}{\omega^3}\left(\omega t - \sin\omega t\right)$

Problems

Determine by contour integration the inverse of the following:

137. $\dfrac{1}{s(s+a)^2}$ 140. $\dfrac{s+2\alpha}{(s+\alpha)^2+\beta^2}$

138. $\dfrac{s+b}{(s+a)^2}$ 141. $\dfrac{1}{s^2(s^2+2\alpha s+\omega^2)}$

139. $\dfrac{1}{s^2(s^2-\omega^2)}$ 142. $\dfrac{s}{(s^2+\omega^2)(s^2+2\alpha s+\omega^2)}$

53. Inversion Involving Branch Points. When the subsidiary function contains branch points, the contour of integration must be altered.

Consider, for example, the function $s^{-\frac{1}{2}}$ which has a branch point at the origin (see Section 25).   If we establish a barrier along the negative x-axis and choose the contour shown in Fig. 86, the path will enclose no singularities and we can write from Cauchy's integral

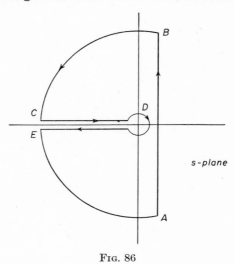

FIG. 86

theorem

$$\int_{AB} \frac{e^{st}\,ds}{s^{\frac{1}{2}}} + \int_{BC+EA} \frac{e^{st}\,ds}{s^{\frac{1}{2}}} + \int_{CDE} \frac{e^{st}\,ds}{s^{\frac{1}{2}}} = 0 \qquad (53.1)$$

Since
$$\lim_{s\to\infty} |s^{-\frac{1}{2}}| = 0$$

the function converges uniformly and satisfies the conditions necessary for the vanishing of the integral around the semicircle of infinite radius.   Equation (53.1) thus reduces to

$$\int_{AB} \frac{e^{st}\,ds}{s^{\frac{1}{2}}} = \int_{EDC} \frac{e^{st}\,ds}{s^{\frac{1}{2}}} \qquad (53.2)$$

where the direction of integration for the second integral has been changed to conform to the positive direction.   We have thus established EDC as an equivalent path to AB.   These paths are frequently referred to as Br$_2$ and Br$_1$, respectively.

The integral along the second Bromwich path Br$_2$ can be evaluated in three parts as follows.   Around the small circle at D we let

$$s = r\,e^{i\theta}$$
$$ds = ir\,e^{i\theta}\,d\theta$$
$$s^{\frac{1}{2}} = r^{\frac{1}{2}}\,e^{i\frac{\theta}{2}}$$

and obtain

$$\int_D \frac{e^{st}}{s^{\frac{1}{2}}}\,ds = i \int_{r \to 0} e^{rt(\cos\theta + i\sin\theta)}\,r^{\frac{1}{2}}\,e^{i\frac{\theta}{2}}\,d\theta = 0 \qquad (53.3)$$

Along ED, we let

$$s = x\,e^{-i\pi} = -x$$
$$ds = -dx$$
$$s^{\frac{1}{2}} = x^{\frac{1}{2}}\,e^{-i\frac{\pi}{2}} = -ix^{\frac{1}{2}}$$

and obtain

$$\int_{ED} \frac{e^{st}\,ds}{s^{\frac{1}{2}}} = -i \int_{+\infty}^{0} x^{-\frac{1}{2}}\,e^{-xt}\,dx = i \int_{0}^{+\infty} x^{-\frac{1}{2}}\,e^{-xt}\,dx \quad (53.4)$$

Along DC, we let

$$s = x\,e^{i\pi} = -x$$
$$ds = -dx$$
$$s^{\frac{1}{2}} = x^{\frac{1}{2}}\,e^{i\frac{\pi}{2}} = ix^{\frac{1}{2}}$$

and obtain

$$\int_{DC} \frac{e^{st}\,ds}{s^{\frac{1}{2}}} = i \int_{0}^{+\infty} x^{-\frac{1}{2}}\,e^{-xt}\,dx \qquad (53.5)$$

Hence the entire integral along Br_2 is equal to

$$2i \int_{0}^{\infty} x^{-\frac{1}{2}}\,e^{-xt}\,dx \qquad (53.6)$$

To reduce this integral to a known form, we let $xt = \lambda^2$:

$$2i \int_{0}^{\infty} x^{-\frac{1}{2}}\,e^{-xt}\,dx = \frac{4i}{\sqrt{t}} \int_{0}^{\infty} e^{-\lambda^2 t}\,d\lambda \qquad (53.7)$$

But from Prob. 74, we have

$$\frac{2}{\sqrt{\pi}} \int_{0}^{\infty} e^{-\lambda^2}\,d\lambda = 1$$

so that our integral is equal to

$$\int_{Br_2} \frac{e^{st}}{s^{\frac{3}{2}}} = 2i \sqrt{\frac{\pi}{t}} \qquad (53.8)$$

The final value of the inversion is then

$$f(t) = \frac{1}{2\pi i} \int_{Br_1} \frac{e^{st}\,ds}{s^{\frac{3}{2}}} = \frac{1}{2\pi i} \int_{Br_2} \frac{e^{st}\,ds}{s^{\frac{3}{2}}} = \frac{1}{\sqrt{\pi t}} \qquad (53.9)$$

Problems

143. Determine a contour for the evaluation of the inverse of

$$\frac{1}{s\sqrt{s+1}}$$

and carry out the contour integration.

144. Evaluate the integral

$$\int_{Br_1} \frac{e^{st}\,e^{-a\sqrt{s}}}{s}\,ds$$

145. Evaluate by contour integration the integral

$$\int \frac{e^{st}\,e^{-\sqrt{\frac{s}{a}}x}}{\sqrt{s^3}}\,ds$$

References

1. Churchill, R. V., *Introduction to Complex Variables and Applications*, McGraw-Hill, 1948.

2. Osgood, W. F., *Functions of a Complex Variable*, Nat. Univ. of Peking Press, 1936.

3. Goursat-Hedrick, *Functions of a Complex Variable*, Ginn & Co.. 1916.

CHAPTER 6

Partial Differential Equations

54. Procedure. The following procedures will be used in the solution of partial differential equations with x and t as independent variables. (1) The Laplace transform is applied with t as a variable, and the partial differential equation is reduced to an ordinary differential equation of the t-transform $\bar{y}(x,s)$ and the independent variable x. The general solution $\bar{y}(x,s)$ of the ordinary differential equation is then fitted to the boundary conditions of the problem, and the final solution $y(x,t)$ is obtained by the application of the complex inversion integral. (2) As an alternative to the first method, iterated transforms are discussed in Sections 71 and 74.

55. String under Arbitrary Displacement. Figure 87 shows an instantaneous position of an element of a perfectly flexible uniform

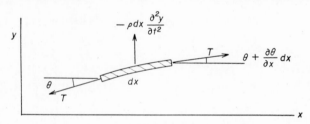

FIG. 87

string under tension T. We shall assume that the deflection y and the angle θ are small and that the tension T is unaffected by the displacement.

Summing forces in the y-direction, we obtain the equation

$$T \left(\theta + \frac{\partial \theta}{\partial x} \, dx \right) - T\theta = \rho \, dx \, \frac{\partial^2 y}{\partial t^2} \tag{55.1}$$

where ρ is the mass per unit length of the string. Since the slope of the string is $\theta = \partial y/\partial x$, the above equation reduces to

117

$$\frac{\partial^2 y}{\partial t^2} = c^2 \frac{\partial^2 y}{\partial x^2} \tag{55.2}$$

which is the partial differential equation of the string with velocity of wave propagation $c = \sqrt{T/\rho}$.

We shall assume now that the string is of infinite length, initially at rest on the x-axis, and that the end $x = 0$ is given a prescribed motion $y(0,t)$.

With the boundary conditions $y(x,0) = \dot{y}(x,0) = 0$, the subsidiary differential equation becomes

$$\frac{d^2 \bar{y}(x,s)}{dx^2} - \left(\frac{s}{c}\right)^2 \bar{y}(x,s) = 0 \tag{55.3}$$

which has a general solution

$$\bar{y}(x,s) = A\, e^{\frac{s}{c}x} + B\, e^{-\frac{s}{c}x} \tag{55.4}$$

To satisfy the condition of zero displacement at $x = \infty$, A must be zero, and the subsidiary solution reduces to

$$\bar{y}(x,s) = B\, e^{-\frac{s}{c}x} \tag{55.5}$$

When $x = 0$, $\bar{y}(x,s)$ becomes equal to the prescribed motion $y(0,t)$; thus $B = \bar{y}(0,s)$ and

$$\bar{y}(x,s) = \bar{y}(0,s)\, e^{-\frac{x}{c}s} \tag{55.6}$$

Making use of the second shifting theorem, we find that the final solution becomes

$$y(x,t) = y\left(0, t - \frac{x}{c}\right) \mathfrak{u}\left(t - \frac{x}{c}\right) \tag{55.7}$$

The interpretation of this equation is as follows. Since

$$\mathfrak{u}\left(t - \frac{x}{c}\right) = 0$$

for $t < x/c$, the string x units from the origin remains at rest until time $t = x/c$, after which it has the same motion as the end $x = 0$. Since c is the velocity of propagation of the disturbance along the string, $t = x/c$ is the time required for the disturbance to reach the point x. Thus point x undergoes the same displacement as the origin, but this displacement lags that of the origin by the time $t = x/c$.

56. Longitudinal Motion of Bars. Consider a uniform bar of cross-sectional area A and modulus of elasticity E. Let p and u be the force per unit area and the displacement of the cross section at x. The corresponding quantities at $x + dx$ are then

$$p + \frac{\partial p}{\partial x}\, dx \quad \text{and} \quad u + \frac{\partial u}{\partial x}\, dx$$

as shown in Fig. 88.

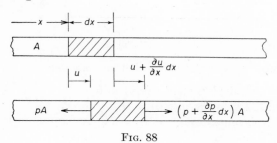

FIG. 88

Summing forces in the x-direction, we have

$$A\, \frac{\partial p}{\partial x}\, dx = \frac{\rho}{g}\, A\, dx\, \frac{\partial^2 u}{\partial t^2} \tag{56.1}$$

where ρ is the weight per unit volume of the material. From Hooke's law, the unit strain (increase in length per unit length) is

$$\frac{\partial u}{\partial x} = \frac{p}{E} \tag{56.2}$$

Combining the two equations, we obtain the wave equation in one space coordinate:

$$\frac{\partial^2 u}{\partial t^2} = c^2\, \frac{\partial^2 u}{\partial x^2} \tag{56.3}$$

where $c = \sqrt{gE/\rho}$ is the propagation velocity of the elastic wave.

When we apply the Laplace transformation, the subsidiary equation becomes an ordinary differential equation:

$$\frac{d^2 \bar{u}(x,s)}{dx^2} = \left(\frac{s}{c}\right)^2 \bar{u}(x,s) - \frac{s}{c^2}\, \bar{u}(x,0) - \frac{1}{c^2}\, u'(x,0) \tag{56.4}$$

After applying the boundary conditions the final solution is obtained by the inverse transformation.

57. Bar Fixed at One End with Prescribed Force on Other End. We shall assume the end $x = 0$ to be fixed and let $F(t)$ be the prescribed force on the end $x = l$, as shown in Fig. 89. We shall also assume that the bar is initially at rest.

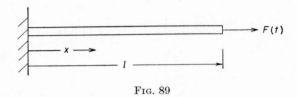

FIG. 89

The boundary equations are then as follows:

$$\left.\begin{array}{l}
\text{Initial displacement } u(x,0) = 0 \\
\text{Initial velocity } u'(x,0) = 0 \\
\text{Displacement at } (x = 0) = 0 \quad \therefore \quad \bar{u}(0,s) = 0 \\
\text{Force at } x = l = F(t) \quad \therefore \quad AE\,\frac{\partial \bar{u}(l,s)}{\partial x} = \bar{F}(s)
\end{array}\right\} \quad (57.1)$$

Substituting these conditions into the subsidiary differential equation, we obtain

$$\bar{u}(x,s) = C_1\,e^{\frac{s}{c}x} + C_2\,e^{-\frac{s}{c}x} \quad (57.2)$$

$$\bar{u}(0,s) = C_1 + C_2 = 0$$

$$AE\,\frac{\partial \bar{u}(l,s)}{\partial x} = AE\,\frac{s}{c}\,(C_1\,e^{\frac{s}{c}l} - C_2\,e^{-\frac{s}{c}l}) = \bar{F}(s)$$

Therefore

$$C_1 = -C_2 = \frac{c\bar{F}(s)}{2AEs\,\cosh\frac{s}{c}l}$$

$$\bar{u}(x,s) = \frac{\bar{F}(s)\,\sinh\frac{s}{c}x}{AE\left(\frac{s}{c}\right)\cosh\frac{s}{c}l} \quad (57.3)$$

Solution for Constant End Force. If a constant force F_0 is suddenly applied to the end of the bar, then $\bar{F}(s) = F_0/s$, and Eq. (57.3) becomes

$$\bar{u}(x,s) = \frac{cF_0}{AE} \frac{\sinh \frac{s}{c} x}{(s)^2 \cosh \frac{s}{c} l} \tag{57.4}$$

The motion of the end $x = l$ is thus readily determined from the transform of Prob. 58, Section 19, as a triangular wave shown in Fig. 90.

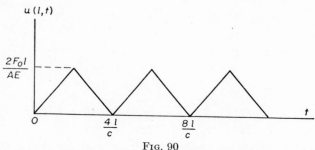

FIG. 90

58. Bar with Prescribed End Motion. We shall now consider the motion of the bar of Fig. 91 with a prescribed motion of the end $x = l$. On the assumption that the bar is initially at rest with

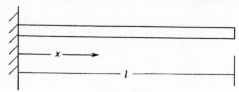

FIG. 91

zero displacement, the subsidiary solution is

$$\bar{u}(x,s) = C_1 e^{\frac{s}{c}x} + C_2 e^{-\frac{s}{c}x} \tag{58.1}$$

Introducing the boundary conditions, we have

$$\bar{u}(0,s) = C_1 + C_2 = 0$$

Therefore
$$C_1 = -C_2 \tag{58.2}$$

$$\bar{u}(l,s) = C_1(e^{\frac{s}{c}l} - e^{-\frac{s}{c}l})$$

$$C_1 = \frac{\bar{u}(l,s)}{2 \sinh \frac{s}{c} l} \tag{58.3}$$

and
$$\bar{u}(x,s) = \frac{\bar{u}(l,s) \sinh \frac{s}{c} x}{\sinh \frac{sl}{c}} \tag{58.4}$$

Sudden Displacement of End $x = l$. If the end $x = l$ is suddenly displaced by u_0, then

$$u(l,t) = u_0 \mathfrak{U}(t) \quad \text{and} \quad \bar{u}(l,s) = \frac{u_0}{s}$$

Substituting into Eq. (58.4), we have

$$\bar{u}(x,s) = \frac{u_0 \sinh \frac{s}{c} x}{s \sinh \frac{s}{c} l} \tag{58.5}$$

Equation (58.5) has only simple poles, since at the origin we have

$$\lim_{s \to 0} \left(\frac{\sinh \frac{s}{c} x}{s} \right) = \frac{x}{c}$$

Thus
$$\left. \begin{array}{l} \sinh \dfrac{sl}{c} = -i \sin i \dfrac{sl}{c} = 0 \\[2mm] i \dfrac{sl}{c} = 0, \ \pm\pi, \ \pm 2\pi, \ \cdots, \ \pm n\pi, \ \cdots \\[2mm] s = \pm i \dfrac{n\pi c}{l} \quad (n = 0, 1, 2, \cdots) \end{array} \right\} \tag{58.6}$$

Thus the displacement expressed by the inversion integral

$$u(x,t) = \frac{u_0}{2\pi i} \int_{-i\infty}^{+i\infty} \frac{e^{st} \sinh \frac{sx}{c}}{s \sinh \frac{sl}{c}} \, ds \tag{58.7}$$

is evaluated as follows:

$$\frac{u_0 \, e^{st} \sinh \dfrac{sx}{c}}{\dfrac{d}{ds} \left(s \sinh \dfrac{sl}{c} \right)} = \left(\frac{u_0 \, e^{st} \sinh \dfrac{sx}{c}}{\dfrac{sl}{c} \cosh \dfrac{sl}{c} + \sinh \dfrac{sl}{c}} \right)_{s = \pm i \frac{n\pi c}{l}}$$

$$= \sum_{n=1}^{\infty} \frac{u_0 \, e^{i\frac{n\pi c}{l}t} \sinh i \dfrac{n\pi x}{l}}{in\pi \cosh in\pi} + \sum_{n=1}^{\infty} \frac{u_0 \, e^{-i\frac{n\pi c}{l}t} \sinh -i \dfrac{n\pi x}{l}}{-in\pi \cosh -in\pi} + u_0 \frac{x}{l}$$

$$= u_0 \sum_{n=1}^{\infty} \frac{\sin \dfrac{n\pi x}{l}}{n\pi \cos n\pi} \left(e^{i\frac{n\pi c}{l}t} + e^{-i\frac{n\pi c}{l}t} \right) + u_0 \frac{x}{l}$$

$$= u_0 \frac{x}{l} + 2u_0 \sum_{n=1}^{\infty} \frac{(-1)^n}{n\pi} \sin \frac{n\pi x}{l} \cos \frac{n\pi c}{l} t$$

The displacement at any point x is then given by the equation

$$u(x,t) = u_0 \left[\frac{x}{l} + 2 \sum_{n=1}^{\infty} \frac{(-1)^n}{n\pi} \sin \frac{n\pi x}{l} \cos \frac{n\pi c}{l} t \right] \qquad (58.8)$$

59. Solution for the Stress in Terms of Reflections. We shall again consider the bar to be fixed at the end $x = 0$ and undergoing a prescribed motion $u(l,t)$ at the end $x = l$. Since the displacement $u(l,t)$ is the time integral of the velocity $v(l,t)$, we can replace $\bar{u}(l,s)$ by $\bar{v}(l,s)/s$ and rewrite Eq. 58.4 as

$$\bar{u}(x,s) = \frac{\bar{v}(l,s) \sinh \dfrac{sx}{c}}{s \sinh \dfrac{sl}{c}} \qquad (59.1)$$

The force being equal to $EA \dfrac{\partial u}{\partial x}$, the subsidiary force equation becomes

$$\bar{F}(x,s) = EA \frac{\partial \bar{u}(x,s)}{\partial x} = \bar{v}(l,s) \left(\frac{AE}{c} \right) \frac{\cosh \dfrac{sx}{c}}{\sinh \dfrac{sl}{c}} \qquad (59.2)$$

Thus the force at the end $x = l$ is determined from the equation

$$\bar{F}(l,s) = \bar{v}(l,s) \left(\frac{AE}{c} \right) \coth \frac{sl}{c}$$

$$= \bar{v}(l,s) \left(\frac{AE}{c} \right) [1 + 2 e^{-2\frac{sl}{c}} + 2 e^{-4\frac{sl}{c}} + 2 e^{-6\frac{sl}{c}} + \cdots \qquad (59.3)$$

By making use of the second shifting theorem, we find that the inverse of this equation is

$$F(l,t) = \left(\frac{AE}{c}\right)\left[v(l,t) + 2v\left(l,t - \frac{2l}{c}\right)\mathfrak{u}\left(t - \frac{2l}{c}\right)\right.$$
$$\left. + 2v\left(l,t - \frac{4l}{c}\right)\mathfrak{u}\left(t - \frac{4l}{c}\right) + \cdots\right] \quad (59.4)$$

This equation is interpreted as follows. Given any prescribed velocity $v(l,t)$ of the end $x = l$, the force at this point is obtained by the superposition of the original velocity with similar velocity of twice the value displaced along the time axis by multiples of the period $2l/c$; that is, the second term represents the reflected force arriving at the end $x = l$ after time $2l/c$, and so on.

FIG. 92

EXAMPLE 59.1: The lower end of a helical spring of length l and stiffness k lb/in., shown in Fig. 92, is subjected to a velocity prescribed by the cam. Determine the force at the cam end.

The stiffness of a uniform bar being AE/l lb/in., the equations of this section apply by letting $AE/l = k$ or

$$F(l,t) = \left(\frac{kl}{c}\right)\left[v(l,t) + 2v\left(l,t - \frac{2l}{c}\right)\mathfrak{u}\left(t - \frac{2l}{c}\right) + \cdots\right]$$

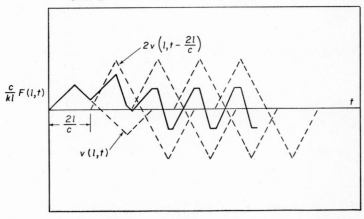

FIG. 93

A plot of the force variation with time is shown in Fig. 93 for a particular $v(l,t)$ curve and period $2l/c$.

Problems

146. A string of length l, fixed at the ends, is under tension T. If at time $t = 0$ the string is given an initial velocity

$$\dot{y}(x,0) = v_0 \sin \frac{\pi x}{l},$$

determine its motion.

147. The end $x = 0$ of a string of length l, fixed at the end $x = l$, is given a prescribed motion $y(0,t)$. Determine the subsidiary solution for the displacement of any point x.

148. The lower end of a helical spring of length l and stiffness k is given a prescribed velocity $v(0,t)$. If the upper end $x = l$ is free, determine the motion of any point x. Develop the equation for the stress in the spring and determine $F(0,t)$ in terms of traveling waves.

149. A helical spring of length l and stiffness k is fixed at the end $x = l$. If the end $x = 0$ is given a velocity $v(0,t) = v_0 \sin \omega t$, determine the stress $F(0,t)$ for (a) $\omega = c/l$, (b) $\omega = \frac{3}{4}c/l$.

150. A helical spring of length l and stiffness k lies unstrained on a horizontal frictionless plane. If a constant force P is applied in the axial direction to the end $x = 0$, determine the motion of any section x.

151. A bar of length l moving with constant velocity v_0 strikes a spring of stiffness k as shown in Fig. 94. Determine the subsidiary solution for

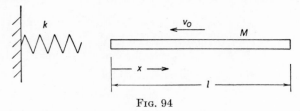

FIG. 94

the displacement $u(x,t)$ measured from the instant the end $x = 0$ strikes the spring.

152. If $l = k = \infty$ in Prob. 151, show that the solution is

$$u(x,t) = -v_0 t + v_0 \left(t - \frac{x}{c} \right) \mathfrak{u} \left(t - \frac{x}{c} \right)$$

153. A uniform rod of length l, fixed at $x = l$, is struck longitudinally on the end $x = 0$ by an impulse of magnitude I_0 lb/sec. Determine its motion and the stress developed.

154. A rod of length l, fixed at $x = 0$, is attached to a dashpot at the end $x = l$, as shown in Fig. 95. If the end $x = l$ is displaced an amount u_0 and released, determine its motion.

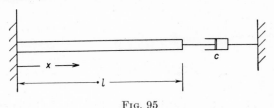

FIG. 95

60. Vibration of a Mass-loaded Rod.

Figure 96 shows a uniform rod of length l and mass m clamped at $x = 0$ and mass-loaded at the end $x = l$. We shall investigate the behavior of such a system to an arbitrary excitation $F(t)$ and determine the parameters governing its motion.

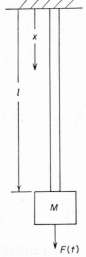

For the uniform bar we have the partial differential equation

$$\frac{\partial^2 u}{\partial t^2} = c^2 \frac{\partial^2 u}{\partial x^2} \tag{60.1}$$

and for the system initially at rest, its transform

$$\frac{d^2 \bar{u}(x,s)}{dx^2} - \left(\frac{s}{c}\right)^2 \bar{u}(x,s) = 0 \tag{60.2}$$

where u is the displacement of an element at x, and $c = \sqrt{Eg/\rho}$.

A subsidiary solution satisfying the boundary condition of $u(0,t) = 0$ is

$$\bar{u}(x,s) = B \sinh \frac{sx}{c} \tag{60.3}$$

FIG. 96

The constant B is evaluated from the boundary condition at $x = l$, which is

$$M\left(\frac{\partial^2 u}{\partial t^2}\right)_{x=l} = F(t) - AE\left(\frac{\partial u}{\partial x}\right)_{x=l} \tag{60.4}$$

or

$$\left[\frac{d\bar{u}(x,s)}{dx}\right]_{x=l} + \frac{Ms^2}{AE}\bar{u}(x,s)_{x=l} = \frac{\bar{F}(s)}{AE} \tag{60.5}$$

Substituting Eq. (60.3) in (60.5) and solving for B, we have

$$B = \frac{F(s)}{\left(\dfrac{AE}{\mu l}\right)\left(\dfrac{sl}{c}\right)\left[\left(\dfrac{sl}{c}\right)\sinh\dfrac{sl}{c} + \mu\cosh\dfrac{sl}{c}\right]} \tag{60.6}$$

$$\mu = \frac{AEl}{Mc^2} = \frac{m}{M} = \text{mass ratio} \tag{60.7}$$

Thus the subsidiary solution is

$$\bar{u}(x,s) = \frac{\bar{F}(s)\sinh\dfrac{sx}{c}}{\left(\dfrac{AE}{\mu l}\right)\left(\dfrac{sl}{c}\right)\left[\left(\dfrac{sl}{c}\right)\sinh\dfrac{sl}{c} + \mu\cosh\dfrac{sl}{c}\right]} \tag{60.8}$$

which is to be evaluated from

$$\frac{1}{\mu}\left(\frac{AE}{l}\right)u(x,t) = \frac{1}{2\pi i}\int_{\gamma-i\infty}^{\gamma+i\infty} \frac{e^{st}\,\bar{F}(s)\sinh\dfrac{sx}{c}\,ds}{\left(\dfrac{sl}{c}\right)\left[\left(\dfrac{sl}{c}\right)\sinh\dfrac{sl}{c} + \mu\cosh\dfrac{sl}{c}\right]} \tag{60.9}$$

We see from this analysis that the parameters entering into the problem are the mass ratio μ and the stiffness (AE/l) of the bar.

61. Evaluation for a Constant Force. If a constant force F_0 is suddenly applied to M at time $t = 0$, $\bar{F}(s) = F_0/s$, and we shall need to evaluate the following inversion:

$$\frac{F_0}{2\pi i}\int_{\gamma-i\infty}^{\gamma+i\infty} \frac{e^{st}\sinh\dfrac{sx}{c}\,ds}{\dfrac{s^2 l}{c}\left[\dfrac{sl}{c}\sinh\dfrac{sl}{c} + \mu\cosh\dfrac{sl}{c}\right]} \tag{61.1}$$

The singular points of the above function are a simple pole at the origin and simple poles obtained from $sl/c \tanh sl/c = -\mu$, which can be rewritten as $\alpha \tan \alpha = \mu$, where $\alpha = i\, sl/c$. The roots α_n, $n = 1, 2, 3, \cdots$ are symmetrically located as shown in Fig. 97.

Evaluating the residue at $s = 0$, we have

$$\left\{\frac{e^{st}\left[\left(\dfrac{sx}{c}\right) + \dfrac{1}{3!}\left(\dfrac{sx}{c}\right)^3 + \cdots\right]}{\left(\dfrac{sl}{c}\right)\left[\left(\dfrac{sl}{c}\right)\sinh\dfrac{sl}{c} + \mu\cosh\dfrac{sl}{c}\right]}\right\}_{s=0} = \frac{x}{\mu l} \tag{61.2}$$

The residues at $s = -i\frac{c}{l}\alpha_n$ are found from

$$\left\{ \frac{e^{st} \sinh \dfrac{sx}{c}}{\dfrac{d}{ds}\dfrac{s^2 l}{c}\left[\dfrac{sl}{c}\sinh\dfrac{sl}{c} + \mu\cosh\dfrac{sl}{c}\right]} \right\}_{s = -i\frac{c}{l}\alpha_n} \tag{61.3}$$

Remembering that the poles $s = -i(c/l)\alpha_n$ are the roots of

$$\frac{sl}{c}\sinh\frac{sl}{c} + \mu\cosh\frac{sl}{c} = 0$$

we find that the denominator of the above expression becomes

$$\left(\frac{sl}{c}\right)^2 \left[\frac{sl}{c}\cosh\frac{sl}{c} + (1 + \mu)\sinh\frac{sl}{c}\right]_{\frac{sl}{c} = -i\alpha_n}$$

$$= -\alpha_n^2[-i\alpha_n\cos\alpha_n - (1 + \mu)i\sin\alpha_n]$$

$$= i\alpha_n^2\left[\alpha_n + (1 + \mu)\frac{\mu}{\alpha_n}\right]\cos\alpha_n \tag{61.4}$$

where $\tan\alpha_n = \mu/\alpha_n$ was used to express $\sin\alpha_n$ in terms of $\cos\alpha_n$.

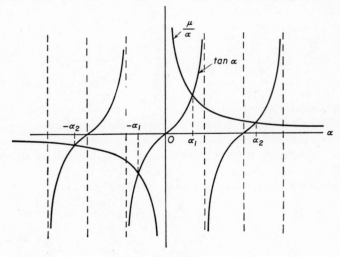

FIG. 97

The sum of all the residues can now be written as

$$\sum \Re = \frac{x}{\mu l} - \sum_{n=\pm 1}^{\pm \infty} \frac{e^{-i\frac{c\alpha_n}{l}t} \sin \alpha_n \frac{x}{l}}{\alpha_n(\alpha_n^2 + \mu + \mu^2) \cos \alpha_n}$$

$$= \frac{x}{\mu l} - \sum_{n=1}^{\infty} \frac{2 \cos \frac{c\alpha_n}{l} t \sin \alpha_n \frac{x}{l}}{\alpha_n(\alpha_n^2 + \mu + \mu^2) \cos \alpha_n} \tag{61.5}$$

Letting $\delta_{st} = F_0 l/AE$, we can write the final solution in non-dimensional form:

$$\frac{u(x,t)}{\delta_{st}} = \frac{x}{l} - 2\mu \sum_{n=1}^{\infty} \frac{\cos \frac{c\alpha_n}{l} t \sin \alpha_n \frac{x}{l}}{\alpha_n(\alpha_n^2 + \mu + \mu^2) \cos \alpha_n} \tag{61.6}$$

Certain conclusions of interest can be obtained from the final solution. If we let $x = l$, the above equation reduces to

$$\frac{u(l,t)}{\delta_{st}} = 1 - 2\mu^2 \sum_{n=1}^{\infty} \frac{\cos \frac{c\alpha_n}{l} t}{\alpha_n^2(\alpha_n^2 + \mu + \mu^2)} \tag{61.7}$$

If μ is small, then $\tan \alpha_1 = \alpha_1 = \mu/\alpha_1$ so the roots are $\alpha = \sqrt{\mu}$, π, 2π, $\cdots$. The solution then becomes

$$\frac{u(l,t)}{\delta_{st}} = 1 - \cos \frac{c \sqrt{\mu}}{l} t - \frac{2\mu^2}{\pi^2} \cos \frac{c\pi}{l} t \cdots$$

$$\cong 1 - \cos \frac{c \sqrt{\mu}}{l} t = 1 - \cos \sqrt{\frac{AE}{lM}} t \tag{61.8}$$

The last equation indicates that the behavior of the system is nearly identical to that of a mass M with a weightless spring of stiffness AE/l lb/in, and that the dynamic load factor is 2 (see Section 28).

Upon investigating the other extreme condition of $\mu \to \infty$, we find that the roots are $\alpha = \frac{\pi}{2}, \frac{3\pi}{2}, \frac{5\pi}{2}, \cdots$, and the solution becomes

$$\frac{u(l,t)}{\delta_{st}} = 1 - \frac{8}{\pi^2} \left[\cos t' + \frac{1}{3^2} \cos 3t' + \frac{1}{5^2} \cos 5t' + \cdots \right] \tag{61.9}$$

where $t' = \pi ct/2l$. This series is recognized as that of a triangular wave of maximum height 2.

62. Motion of Engine Valves. Figure 98 shows an engine valve whose lower end undergoes a motion prescribed by the cam. It will be of interest here to determine the stress at the end $x = 0$. If this becomes negative, the valve will leave the cam and produce pitting as it repeatedly strikes the cam. Since the stress in the spring is known for any prescribed motion of the lower end (see Section 59), we can treat this problem in two parts. We shall deal now with the valve alone.

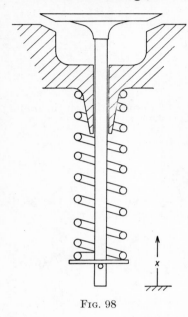

Starting with the subsidiary solution for a uniform rod,

$$\bar{u}(x,s) = B \sinh \frac{sx}{c} + D \cosh \frac{sx}{c}$$

(62.1)

Fig. 98

where $u(x,t)$ is the displacement of any point x measured from the lower end, we apply the boundary conditions, which are as follows:

At $x = 0$, the displacement is the prescribed displacement $u(0,t)$ of the cam:

$$\bar{u}(0,s) = D$$

(62.2)

At the end $x = l$, the force on the rod is equal to the inertia force of the end mass M:

$$\bar{F}(l,s) = AE \frac{d\bar{u}(x,s)}{dx} = -Ms^2\bar{u}(l,s) \qquad (x = l) \qquad (62.3)$$

$$AE \frac{s}{c} \left[B \cosh \frac{sl}{c} + \bar{u}(0,s) \sinh \frac{sl}{c} \right]$$

$$= -Ms^2 \left[B \sinh \frac{sl}{c} + \bar{u}(0,s) \cosh \frac{sl}{c} \right]$$

The constant B is thus evaluated to be

$$B = \frac{-\bar{u}(0,s)\left(\cosh\dfrac{sl}{c} + \dfrac{AE}{Mcs}\sinh\dfrac{sl}{c}\right)}{\left(\sinh\dfrac{sl}{c} + \dfrac{AE}{Mcs}\cosh\dfrac{sl}{c}\right)} \tag{62.4}$$

The term AE/Mcs appearing in B can be reduced to the following:

$$\frac{AE}{Mcs} = \frac{AEl}{Mc^2}\frac{c}{sl} = \frac{Al\rho}{M}\frac{c}{sl} = \mu\frac{c}{sl} \tag{62.5}$$

where μ is the mass ratio of the valve stem to the valve head. The subsidiary force at the end $x = 0$ now becomes

$$\bar{F}(0,s) = \frac{AEs}{c}B = -\bar{u}(0,s)\left(\frac{AE}{l}\right)\left(\frac{sl}{c}\right)\frac{\left(\mu\sinh\dfrac{sl}{c} + \dfrac{sl}{c}\cosh\dfrac{sl}{c}\right)}{\left(\dfrac{sl}{c}\sinh\dfrac{sl}{c} + \mu\cosh\dfrac{sl}{c}\right)} \tag{62.6}$$

Evaluation for Constant Acceleration of End. If we know the force $F(0,t)$ for a constant acceleration a of the end $x = 0$, we can determine the force $F(0,t)$ due to any motion composed of combinations of constant accelerations. The displacement corresponding to a constant acceleration a being $u(0,t) = at^2/2$, $\bar{u}(0,s) = a/s^3$. Equation (62.6) can then be written as

$$\bar{F}(0,s) = -\left(\frac{AE}{l}\right)\left(\frac{l}{c}\right)\frac{a}{s^2}\left(\frac{\mu\sinh\dfrac{sl}{c} + \dfrac{sl}{c}\cosh\dfrac{sl}{c}}{\dfrac{sl}{c}\sinh\dfrac{sl}{c} + \mu\cosh\dfrac{sl}{c}}\right) \tag{62.7}$$

which has simple poles at $s = 0$ and $sl/c\ \tanh\ sl/c = -\mu$ (see preceding problem, Section 61). With the same notation as in the previous problem, $\alpha\tan\alpha = \mu$, where $\alpha = isl/c$. The evaluation of the inverse transformation follows a procedure similar to Section 61, the result being

$$-\frac{F(0)}{Ma} = (1 + \mu) - 2\mu\sum_{n=1}^{\infty}\left(1 + \frac{\mu^2}{\alpha_n^2}\right)\frac{\cos\alpha_n\dfrac{ct}{l}}{(\mu + \mu^2 + \alpha_n^2)} \tag{62.8}$$

Analysis of this result shows that the first term $(1 + \mu)Ma$

$= (m + M)a$ is the force required to accelerate the rigid body. The remaining terms represented by the series constitute the oscillatory force.

It will be of interest here to examine the result for limiting cases of the mass ratio μ. If μ is very small, $\alpha_1^2 = \mu$, and the above equation reduces to

$$\frac{F(0,t)}{Ma} \cong 1 - \cos \sqrt{\mu} \frac{ct}{l}$$

$$= 1 - \cos \sqrt{\frac{EA}{lM}}\, t \qquad (62.9)$$

This is the result one would expect for a mass M at the end of a spring of stiffness $k = EA/l$.

If μ is very large, we obtain the equation

$$\frac{F(0,t)}{(m + M)a} = 1 - 2 \sum_{n=1}^{\infty} \frac{\cos \alpha_n \dfrac{ct}{l}}{\alpha_n^2} \qquad (62.10)$$

The effect of the valve spring is to keep the lower end of the valve in contact with the cam. Since the force at the lower end of the spring is known for any prescribed motion of the valve stem (see Sections 58 and 59), the resultant cam force is determined by the superposition of the spring force and the force given by Eq. (62.8).

63. Resonant Frequencies. A subsidiary function of the type $1/(s^2 + \omega^2)^2$ which has a second-order pole at $s = \pm i\omega$ will always result in a diverging time function. For instance, applying the residue theorem, we have

$$\mathcal{L}^{-1} \frac{1}{(s^2 + \omega^2)^2} = \left(\frac{d}{ds}\, e^{st}\right)_{s=\pm i\omega} = 2t \cos \omega t \qquad (63.1)$$

Consider next a subsidiary function of the form

$$\frac{A(s)}{(s^2 + \omega^2)Z(s)} \qquad (63.2)$$

If the roots of $Z(s) = 0$ are imaginary and symmetrically displaced about the origin, it is possible to have one of them coincide with ω, in which case we would have a second-order pole at $s = \pm i\omega$ and a diverging time function.

As an example, let the force applied to the system of Fig. 96 be sinusoidal $F(t) = F_0 \sin \omega t$. The subsidiary equation (60.8) then becomes

$$\bar{u}(x,s) = \frac{\omega F_0 \sinh sx/c}{\left(\dfrac{AE}{\mu l}\right)(s^2 + \omega^2)\left(\dfrac{sl}{c}\right)\left[\left(\dfrac{sl}{c}\right)\sinh \dfrac{sl}{c} + \mu \cosh \dfrac{sl}{c}\right]} \quad (63.3)$$

The poles in this expression are

$$s = \pm i\omega \quad \text{and} \quad s = \pm i \cdot \frac{\alpha_n c}{l}$$

where α_n are the positive roots of the equation $\alpha \tan \alpha = \mu$. Thus, if ω coincides with one of the roots $\alpha_k c/l$, a second order pole is encountered, resulting in resonance. It is evident, then, that the resonant frequencies of the system of Fig. 96 are $\omega_n = \alpha_n c/l$.

Problems

155. For the mass-loaded uniform rod clamped at one end and excited at the other end, derive the subsidiary equation for the stress at any point.

156. For a constant force F_0 applied at the end, show that the stress equation becomes

$$\frac{F(x,t)}{F_{st}(l)} = 1 - 2\mu \sum_{n=1}^{\infty} \frac{\cos \alpha_n \dfrac{x}{l} \cos \alpha_n \dfrac{ct}{l}}{(\alpha_n^2 + \mu + \mu^2) \cos \alpha_n}$$

157. For $\mu = 0.20$, show that Eq. (61.7) becomes

$$\frac{u(l,t)}{\delta_{st}} = 1 - 0.99 \cos 0.433 \frac{ct}{l} - 0.00074 \cos 3.20 \frac{ct}{l} \cdots$$

158. Determine the equation of motion for the mass loaded rod of Fig. 96 if the lower end is displaced by an amount u_0 and released. Establish the equation for the natural frequencies of the system.

159. For $\mu = 0.20$, show that Eq. (62.8) becomes

$$-\frac{F(0,t)}{Ma} = 1.20 - 1.135 \cos 0.433t' - 0.379 \cos 3.20t' - \cdots$$

where $t' = ct/l$.

160. Determine the resonant frequencies of a uniform bar of length l fixed at one end and free at the other end.

161. Determine the resonant frequencies of a uniform bar of length l if one end terminates to a spring of stiffness k as shown in Fig. 99. *Hint:* Write the subsidiary equation with a sinusoidal impressed force at the end $x = l$.

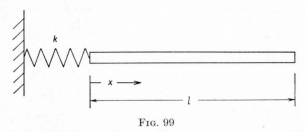

Fig. 99

64. Water Hammer. When the flow of liquid in a pipe is subjected to a sudden change, a surge of pressure wave, referred to as *water hammer*, is developed. We shall derive the differential equations describing this phenomenon and examine the solution for various types of valve closure.

Figure 100 shows a pipe of length l backed up by a reservoir and terminating with a valve which regulates the flow. A sudden

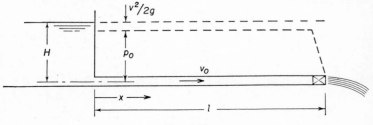

Fig. 100

closure of the valve results in a pressure wave which travels from the valve to the reservoir with a velocity c which is considerably greater than the velocity of flow v. This surge of pressure results in the compression of the liquid and a dilatation of the pipe.

Figure 101 shows a section of the liquid when the pressure wave has just reached the forward end of the element under consideration. Neglecting friction in the pipe and summing forces acting on the element, we have

$$-A\,\frac{\partial p}{\partial x}\,dx = \frac{\rho}{g}\,A\,dx\,\frac{\partial v}{\partial t} \tag{64.1}$$

where A is the cross-sectional area of the pipe, ρ the weight per unit volume of the liquid, and p and v the pressure and the velocity of flow, respectively.

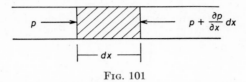

Fɪɢ. 101

The second equation relating velocity and pressure is obtained by examining a given quantity of fluid in the two positions shown in Fig. 102.   If we let v be the velocity of flow at A, the velocity at B will be $v + (\partial v/\partial x)\,dx$.   If the element AB moves to position CD in time dt, we have

$$\left.\begin{aligned} v_C &= v + \frac{\partial v}{\partial t}\,dt + \frac{\partial v}{\partial x}\,v\,dt \\ v_D &= v + \frac{\partial v}{\partial x}\,dx + \frac{\partial v}{\partial t}\,dt + \frac{\partial v}{\partial x}\,v\,dt \end{aligned}\right\} \qquad (64.2)$$

The distances AC and BD can then be determined by taking the

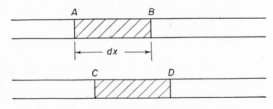

Fɪɢ. 102

average velocity and multiplying by the time:

$$\left.\begin{aligned} \overline{AC} &= \tfrac{1}{2}(v + v_C)\,dt \\ \overline{BD} &= \tfrac{1}{2}\left(v + \frac{\partial v}{\partial x}\,dx + v_D\right)dt \end{aligned}\right\} \qquad (64.3)$$

Hence the reduction in the length dx is

$$\overline{AC} - \overline{BD} = \frac{1}{2}\left(-\frac{\partial v}{\partial x}\,dx + v_C - v_D\right)dt = -\frac{\partial v}{\partial x}\,dx\,dt \quad (64.4)$$

The reduction in the length dx, designated by Δ, can also be expressed in terms of the pressure and the properties of the pipe. From the conservation of mass we have

$$\rho A \, dx = (\rho + d\rho)(A + dA)(dx + \Delta) \tag{64.5}$$

If we neglect higher-order terms, this equation reduces to

$$\Delta = \left(\frac{d\rho}{\rho} + \frac{dA}{A}\right) dx \tag{64.6}$$

We now express $d\rho/\rho$ and dA/A in terms of the pressure and diameter. Since

$$\rho V = \text{constant}$$

where V is the volume, we have, on differentiating,

$$\frac{d\rho}{\rho} = -\frac{dV}{V} = \frac{dp}{K} \tag{64.7}$$

where the last term is introduced by the definition of the bulk modulus K of the fluid.

The change in cross-sectional area can be expressed in terms of the diameter from the equation

$$A = \frac{\pi D^2}{4}$$
$$\frac{dA}{A} = 2\frac{dD}{D} \tag{64.8}$$

Since dD/D is the unit strain, it is also equal to the ratio of the

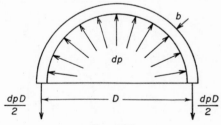

Fig. 103

stress to the modulus of elasticity. Referring to Fig. 103, we find that the stress is $(dp/2)(D/b)$, from which

$$\frac{dA}{A} = 2\frac{dD}{D} = \frac{dpD}{bE} \tag{64.9}$$

Substituting back into Eq. (64.6) we obtain

$$\Delta = \left(\frac{1}{K} + \frac{D}{bE}\right) dx \, dp \tag{64.10}$$

Equating Eqs. (64.4) and (64.10), we obtain

$$-\frac{\partial v}{\partial x} = \left(\frac{1}{K} + \frac{D}{bE}\right)\frac{\partial p}{\partial t} \tag{64.11}$$

Differentiating Eq. (64.11) with respect to t and Eq. (64.1) with respect to x and eliminating $\partial^2 v/\partial x \, \partial t$, we obtain the wave equation for the surge pressure

$$\frac{\partial^2 p}{\partial t^2} = c^2 \frac{\partial^2 p}{\partial x^2} \tag{64.12}$$

where

$$c = \sqrt{\frac{g}{\rho\left(\frac{1}{K} + \frac{D}{bE}\right)}} \tag{64.13}$$

is the velocity of propagation of the pressure wave.

Approximate values of E for the usual pipe material are as follows:

Wrought iron.............................. 26×10^6 lb/in²
Wrought steel............................. 28×10^6 lb/in²
Cast iron................................. 12×10^6 lb/in²

and for any material and fluid, the velocity of propagation becomes a function of D/b as shown by the following table for wrought-steel pipes filled with water.[*]

VELOCITY OF PRESSURE WAVE FOR WATER
IN WROUGHT-STEEL PIPES

$\dfrac{D}{b}$	c ft/sec
100	3280
200	2340
for $E = \infty$	4720

65. Instantaneous Valve Closure. If we let $\bar{p}(x,s)$ be the Laplace transform of the pressure, Eq. (64.12) transforms to

$$c^2 \frac{d^2\bar{p}(x,s)}{dx^2} - s^2\bar{p}(x,s) = sp(x,0) - p'(x,0) \tag{65.1}$$

Since the pressure and its time rate of change at $t = 0$ are $p(x,0) = p_0$ and $p'(x,0) = 0$, the subsidiary solution for $\bar{p}(x,s)$ becomes

$$\bar{p}(x,s) = C_1 \cosh \frac{s}{c} x + C_2 \sinh \frac{s}{c} x + \frac{p_0}{s} \tag{65.2}$$

[*] M. P. O'Brien and G. H. Hickox, *Applied Fluid Mechanics*, McGraw-Hill, 1937, page 246.

For the second equation we start with Eq. (64.1),

$$-\frac{\partial p}{\partial x} = \frac{\rho}{g}\frac{\partial v}{\partial t} \tag{65.3}$$

and write its subsidiary form

$$\frac{d\bar{p}(x,s)}{dx} = -\frac{\rho}{g}[s\bar{v}(x,s) - v(x,0)] \tag{65.4}$$

With instantaneous valve closure we have the following boundary conditions:

(1) At the reservoir $x = 0$, the pressure is p_0:

$$\bar{p}(0,s) = \frac{p_0}{s} \tag{65.5}$$

(2) At the valve $x = l$, the initial velocity v_0 is suddenly reduced to zero:

$$v(l,0) = v_0$$
$$v(l,t) = 0$$
Therefore $\quad\quad\quad\bar{v}(l,s) = 0 \tag{65.6}$

Substituting Eq. (65.2) in Eq. (65.5), we have

$$\frac{p_0}{s} = C_1 + \frac{p_0}{s}$$

Therefore $\quad\quad\quad C_1 = 0$

Substituting Eq. (65.2) in Eq. (65.4) and letting $x = l$ with the boundary conditions (2), we have

$$C_2 = \frac{\rho}{g}\frac{cv_0}{s\cosh\dfrac{sl}{c}}$$

The subsidiary solution is then

$$\bar{p}(x,s) = \frac{p_0}{s} + \frac{\rho}{g}\frac{cv_0\sinh\dfrac{sx}{c}}{s\cosh\dfrac{sl}{c}} \tag{65.7}$$

and the final solution is determined from the inversion integral

$$p(x,t) = \frac{p_0}{2\pi i}\int_{\gamma-i\infty}^{\gamma+i\infty}\frac{e^{st}}{s}\,ds + \frac{\rho cv_0}{2\pi ig}\int_{\gamma-i\infty}^{\gamma+i\infty}\frac{e^{st}\sinh\dfrac{sx}{c}}{s\cosh\dfrac{sl}{c}}\,ds \tag{65.8}$$

66. Evaluation of the Inversion Integral. The first integral of Eq. (65.8) has a simple pole at $s = 0$. Its residue is

$$\lim_{s \to 0} e^{st} = 1.0 \tag{66.1}$$

and hence the first term is p_0.

In the second integral, the poles are the roots of the equation

$$\left. \begin{array}{c} \cosh \dfrac{sl}{c} = \cos i \dfrac{sl}{c} = 0 \\[2mm] \text{or} \qquad \dfrac{sl}{c} = \pm i(2k - 1) \dfrac{\pi}{2} \quad (k = 1, 2, 3, \cdots) \end{array} \right\} \tag{66.2}$$

Since the limit

$$\lim_{s \to 0} \frac{\sinh \dfrac{sx}{c}}{s} = \frac{x}{c} \tag{66.3}$$

there is no pole at $s = 0$ for this integral.

The residues for the second integral are thus

$$\left\{ \frac{e^{st} \sinh \dfrac{sx}{c}}{\dfrac{d}{ds} s \cosh \dfrac{sl}{c}} \right\}_{s=\text{roots}} = \left\{ \frac{e^{st} \sinh \dfrac{sx}{c}}{\dfrac{sl}{c} \sinh \dfrac{sl}{c} + \cosh \dfrac{sl}{c}} \right\}_{s = \pm i(2k-1)\frac{\pi c}{2l}}$$

$$= \sum_{k=1}^{\infty} \frac{e^{i(2k-1)\frac{\pi ct}{2l}} \sinh i(2k - 1) \dfrac{\pi x}{2l}}{i(2k - 1) \dfrac{\pi}{2} \sinh i(2k - 1) \dfrac{\pi}{2}}$$

$$+ \sum_{k=1}^{\infty} \frac{e^{-i(2k-1)\frac{\pi ct}{2l}} \sinh -i(2k - 1) \dfrac{\pi x}{2l}}{-i(2k - 1) \dfrac{\pi}{2} \sinh -i(2k - 1) \dfrac{\pi}{2}}$$

$$= \sum_{k=1}^{\infty} \frac{2 \sin (2k - 1) \dfrac{\pi x}{2l}}{(2k - 1) \dfrac{\pi}{2} \sin (2k - 1) \dfrac{\pi}{2}} \left(\frac{e^{i(2k-1)\frac{\pi ct}{2l}} - e^{-i(2k-1)\frac{\pi ct}{2l}}}{2i} \right)$$

$$= \frac{4}{\pi} \sum_{k=1}^{\infty} \frac{(-1)^{k-1}}{(2k - 1)} \sin (2k - 1) \frac{\pi x}{2l} \sin (2k - 1) \frac{\pi ct}{2l} \tag{66.4}$$

The final solution then becomes

$$p(x,t) = p_0 + \frac{\rho}{g} \frac{cv_0 4}{\pi} \sum_{k=1}^{\infty} \frac{(-1)^{k-1}}{(2k-1)} \sin (2k-1) \frac{\pi x}{2l} \sin (2k-1) \frac{\pi ct}{2l}$$

(66.5)

The pressure at the valve is readily obtained from the above equation for $x = l$, as

$$p(l,t) = p_0 + \frac{\rho cv_0}{g} \frac{4}{\pi} \left(\sin \frac{\pi ct}{2l} + \frac{1}{3} \sin \frac{3\pi ct}{2l} + \frac{1}{5} \sin \frac{5\pi ct}{2l} + \cdots \right)$$

(66.6)

which is a rectangular wave as shown in Fig. 104.

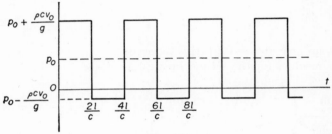

FIG. 104

67. Solution in Terms of Traveling Waves.

The solution of Eq. (65.8) can be expressed in terms of traveling waves by replacing the hyperbolic functions by exponentials. Equation (65.8) then takes the form

$$p(x,t) = \frac{p_0}{2\pi i} \int_{\gamma-i\infty}^{\gamma+i\infty} \frac{e^{st}}{s} \, ds + \frac{\rho cv_0}{2\pi ig} \int_{\gamma-i\infty}^{\gamma+i\infty} \frac{e^{st} e^{-\frac{sl}{c}} (e^{\frac{sx}{c}} - e^{-\frac{sx}{c}}) \, ds}{s(1 + e^{-\frac{2sl}{c}})}$$

(67.1)

since $\quad (1 + e^{-\frac{2sl}{c}})^{-1} = 1 - e^{-\frac{2sl}{c}} + e^{-\frac{4sl}{c}} - e^{-\frac{6sl}{c}} + \cdots$

$$p(x,t) = p_0 + \frac{\rho cv_0}{2\pi ig} \int_{\gamma-i\infty}^{\gamma+i\infty}$$

$$[e^{s\left(t-\frac{l}{c}+\frac{x}{c}\right)} - e^{s\left(t-\frac{l}{c}-\frac{x}{c}\right)} - e^{s\left(t-\frac{3l}{c}+\frac{x}{c}\right)} + e^{s\left(t-\frac{3l}{c}-\frac{x}{c}\right)} + \cdots] \frac{ds}{s}$$

$$= p_0 + \frac{\rho c v_0}{g} \left[\mathfrak{u}\left(t - \frac{l-x}{c}\right) - \mathfrak{u}\left(t - \frac{l+x}{c}\right) \right.$$
$$\left. - \mathfrak{u}\left(t - \frac{3l-x}{c}\right) + \mathfrak{u}\left(t - \frac{3l+x}{c}\right) + \cdots \right] \quad (67.2)$$

This solution is interpreted as follows. When the valve is suddenly closed, a pressure wave equal to $\rho c v_0/g$ travels towards the reservoir with speed c. The first wave which is a positive pressure reaches the point x ft from the reservoir in time $(l - x)/c$. At the reservoir the wave is reflected as a negative pressure $-\rho c v_0/g$. As is indicated

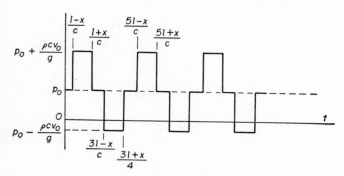

FIG. 105

by the second term, the time required for this negative pressure to reach point x is $(l + x)/c$. This wave is reflected at the valve without change in sign and reaches x in time $(3l - x)/c$, and so on. To summarize, the pressure p_0 at x suddenly increases to $p_0 + (\rho c v_0/g)$ at time $t = (l - x)/c$ and remains unchanged until time $t = (l + x)/c$, when the negative pressure nullifies the positive pressure, leaving it equal to p_0 until $t = (3l - x)/c$. The pressure then becomes $p_0 - (\rho c v_0/g)$ until time $t = (3l + x)/c$ when it becomes p_0 again, and so on. The result is illustrated graphically in Fig. 105. If $x = l$, this curve reduces to that of Fig. 104.

68. Linear Valve Closure. If the valve is closed in such a way that the velocity of flow is reduced linearly from v_0 to 0 in time τ, as shown in Fig. 106, the boundary conditions and the corresponding subsidiary form are as follows:

At the valve $x = l$:

$$v(0) = v_0$$

$$\left.\begin{array}{ll} v(t) = v_0\left(1 - \dfrac{t}{\tau}\right)_{0<t<\tau} & \bar{v}(s) = v_0\left(\dfrac{1}{s} - \dfrac{1}{\tau s^2}\right) \\[2mm] v(t) = 0_{t>\tau} & \bar{v}(s) = v_0\left(\dfrac{1}{s} - \dfrac{1}{\tau s^2}\right) + \dfrac{v_0\,e^{-s\tau}}{\tau s^2} \end{array}\right\} \quad (68.1)$$

At the reservoir $x = 0$:

$$p(0,t) = p_0 \tag{68.2}$$

When we substitute these boundary conditions into Eqs. (65.2)

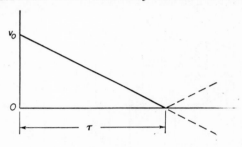

FIG. 106

and (65.4),

$$C_1 = 0$$

and

$$\left.\begin{array}{l} C_2 = \dfrac{\rho v_0 c}{g\tau s^2 \cosh sl/c}_{\,0<t<\tau} \\[3mm] = \dfrac{\rho v_0 c(1 - e^{-s\tau})}{g\tau s^2 \cosh sl/c}_{\,t>\tau} \end{array}\right\} \tag{68.3}$$

The subsidiary equations are thus

$$\left.\begin{array}{l} \bar{p}(x,s) = \dfrac{p_0}{s} + \left(\dfrac{\rho v_0 c}{g\tau}\right)\dfrac{\sinh sx/c}{s^2 \cosh sl/c}_{\,0<t<\tau} \\[3mm] \phantom{\bar{p}(x,s)} = \dfrac{p_0}{s} + (1 - e^{-s\tau})\left(\dfrac{\rho v_0 c}{g\tau}\right)\dfrac{\sinh sx/c}{s^2 \cosh sl/c}_{\,t>\tau} \end{array}\right\} \tag{68.4}$$

from which the solution is obtained as

$$p(x,t) = p_0 + \frac{\rho c v_0}{g\tau}\left[\frac{x}{c} - \frac{8l}{c\pi^2}\sum_{k=1}^{\infty}\frac{(-1)^{k-1}}{(2k - 1)^2}\sin(2k - 1)\frac{\pi x}{2l}\right.$$

$$\left.\cos(2k - 1)\frac{\pi c t}{2l}\right]_{0<t<\tau} \tag{68.5}$$

$$= p_0 + \frac{\rho c v_0}{g\tau} \left[\frac{x}{c} - \frac{8l}{c\pi^2} \sum_{k=1}^{\infty} \frac{(-1)^{k-1}}{(2k-1)^2} \sin (2k-1) \frac{\pi x}{2l} \right.$$

$$\cos (2k-1) \frac{\pi c t}{2l} \left] - \frac{\rho c v_0}{g\tau} \left[\frac{x}{c} - \frac{8l}{c\pi^2} \sum_{k=1}^{\infty} \frac{(-1)^{k-1}}{(2k-1)^2} \sin (2k-1) \frac{\pi x}{2l} \right.$$

$$\cos (2k-1) \frac{\pi c(t-\tau)}{2l} \left]_{t>\tau} \mathfrak{u}(t-\tau) \quad (68.6)$$

References

1. Rich, G. R., "Water Hammer Analysis by the Laplace-Mellin Transformation," *Trans. ASME*, **67**, 5 (1945), pages 361–376.

2. Wood, F. M., "The Application of Heaviside's Operational Calculus to the Solution of Problems in Water Hammer," *Trans. ASME*, **59**, 8 (1937), pages 707–713.

Problems

162. Determine the equation for the velocity $v(x,t)$ for the case of instantaneous valve closure.

163. Express the hyperbolic functions in Eq. (68.4) by exponentials and determine the solution in terms of the traveling waves.

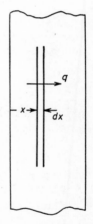

FIG. 107

69. Conduction of Heat. The general problem of heat conduction was first treated mathematically by Fourier. In this section we shall take up the simple case of unidirectional flow of heat through a rectangular slab of uniform thickness. To find the temperature at any point at any time, we shall need to define the following quantities with reference to Fig. 107.

U = temperature difference between the planes at x and $x = 0$, the two planes being parallel and perpendicular to the direction of flow of heat

q = quantity of heat flowing across a unit area in unit time

k = thermal conductivity of the material = the quantity of heat flowing across a unit area per unit time when the temperature gradient $\partial U/\partial x = 1.0$

c = specific heat per unit mass, that is, the quantity of heat necessary to raise the temperature of a unit mass of the material one degree

The flow of heat q per unit area per unit time is proportional to the temperature gradient and the thermal conductivity of the material. Thus across the plane at x, the flow is

$$q_x = -k \frac{\partial U}{\partial x} \tag{69.1}$$

whereas across a parallel plane at $x + dx$ we have

$$q_{x+dx} = -k \frac{\partial}{\partial x} \left(U + \frac{\partial U}{\partial x} dx \right) \tag{69.2}$$

The difference in the flow of heat across these two planes per unit time is the rate of absorption of heat by the element $1 \times 1 \times dx$:

$$q_x - q_{x+dx} = k \frac{\partial^2 U}{\partial x^2} dx = c\rho \, dx \frac{\partial U}{\partial t} \tag{69.3}$$

and the partial differential equation for the problem becomes

$$\frac{\partial U}{\partial t} = a \frac{\partial^2 U}{\partial x^2} \tag{69.4}$$

where $a = k/c\rho$ is the thermal diffusivity of the material.

70. Semi-infinite Block of Zero Temperature Subjected to a Constant Temperature U_0 at $x = 0$. The equation

$$\frac{\partial U}{\partial t} = a \frac{\partial^2 U}{\partial x^2}$$

is to be solved for the boundary conditions

$$\left. \begin{array}{ll} U(x,0) = 0 & \bar{U}(x,0) = 0 \\ U(0,t) = U_0 & \bar{U}(0,s) = \dfrac{U_0}{s} \\ U(\infty,t) = 0 & \bar{U}(\infty,s) = 0 \end{array} \right\} \tag{70.1}$$

The subsidiary equation then becomes

$$\frac{d^2 \bar{U}(x,s)}{dx^2} - \frac{s}{a} \bar{U}(x,s) = 0 \tag{70.2}$$

This equation has the solution

$$\bar{U}(x,s) = A e^{-\sqrt{\frac{s}{a}}x} + B e^{\sqrt{\frac{s}{a}}x} \tag{70.3}$$

and we see immediately that B must be zero to satisfy the boundary condition at infinity. A is then evaluated at the boundary $x = 0$ as

$$A = \frac{U_0}{s} \tag{70.4}$$

and the solution in the subsidiary domain becomes

$$\bar{U}(x,s) = \frac{U_0}{s} e^{-\sqrt{\frac{s}{a}}x} \tag{70.5}$$

From Eq. (25.21), Section 25, the final solution is

$$U(x,t) = U_0 \left[1 - \text{erf}\left(\frac{x}{2\sqrt{at}}\right) \right] \tag{70.6}$$

71. Iterated Transforms. Iterated transforms can be used to solve partial differential equations. We shall take up the application of this method to a problem in heat conduction.

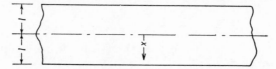

Fɪɢ. 108

Consider the problem of determining the temperature distribution of an infinite slab of thickness $2l$ (shown in Fig. 108) initially at a uniform temperature U_0 and suddenly submerged in a cold medium the temperature of which is held constant. For convenience we shall let the temperature of the cold medium be zero.

We have for this case the differential equation

$$\frac{\partial U}{\partial t} = a \frac{\partial^2 U}{\partial x^2} \tag{71.1}$$

and the following boundary conditions:

(1) The initial temperature is constant:

$$U(x,0) = U_0, \quad \bar{U}(x,0) = \frac{U_0}{s} \tag{71.2}$$

(2) Because of symmetry, the temperature gradient at $x = 0$ is zero at all times; that is, the problem is identical to that of a slab of thickness l insulated on the face $x = 0$ and subjected to a cold medium on the face $x = l$.

$$\frac{\partial U(0,t)}{\partial x} = 0, \quad \frac{\partial \overline{U}(0,s)}{\partial x} = 0 \tag{71.3}$$

(3) The rate of heat flow at the face $x = l$ is proportional to the difference in temperature of the face $x = l$ and that of the medium.

$$q = -k' \frac{\partial U(l,t)}{\partial x} = fU(l,t)$$

$$\frac{\partial U(l,t)}{\partial x} = -hU(l,t) \tag{71.4}$$

where f is the equivalent film thickness adjacent to the plate, k' is the equivalent conductivity of this film, and h is the ratio f/k'. This last equation is the mathematical statement of *Newton's law of cooling*. Its transform is

$$\frac{\partial \overline{U}(l,s)}{\partial x} = -h\overline{U}(l,s) \tag{71.5}$$

Taking the transform of Eq. (71.1) and using boundary condition (1), we have

$$\frac{d^2\overline{U}(x,s)}{dx^2} - \frac{s}{a}\overline{U}(x,s) = -\frac{U_0}{a} \tag{71.6}$$

Instead of writing the solution to this equation as is usually done, we now take the transform of this equation with respect to x, using another bar and the letter p for the subsidiary variable of x:

$$p^2\overline{\overline{U}}(p,s) - p\overline{U}(0,s) - \frac{d\overline{U}(0,s)}{dx} - \frac{s}{a}\overline{\overline{U}}(p,s) = -\frac{U_0}{ap} \tag{71.7}$$

From boundary condition (2), the third term on the left side of this equation is zero, and the result can be arranged in the form

$$\overline{\overline{U}}(p,s) = \frac{p\overline{U}(0,s)}{\left(p^2 - \dfrac{s}{a}\right)} - \frac{U_0}{ap\left(p^2 - \dfrac{s}{a}\right)} \tag{71.8}$$

Taking the inverse with respect to x, we obtain

$$\bar{U}(x,s) = \bar{U}(0,s) \cosh \sqrt{\frac{s}{a}}\, x + \frac{U_0}{s}\left(1 - \cosh \sqrt{\frac{s}{a}}\, x\right) \quad (71.9)$$

Differentiating with respect to x and substituting into the equation for the third boundary condition, we can evaluate the quantity $\bar{U}(0,s)$ as

$$\bar{U}(0,s) = \frac{U_0}{s}\left\{1 - \frac{1}{\left(\frac{1}{h}\sqrt{\frac{s}{a}} \sinh \sqrt{\frac{s}{a}}\, l + \cosh \sqrt{\frac{s}{a}}\, l\right)}\right\} \quad (71.10)$$

Substituting this quantity back into Eq. (71.9), we have

$$\bar{U}(x,s) = \frac{U_0}{s} - \frac{U_0 \cosh \sqrt{\frac{s}{a}}\, x}{s\left(\frac{1}{h}\sqrt{\frac{s}{a}} \sinh \sqrt{\frac{s}{a}}\, l + \cosh \sqrt{\frac{s}{a}}\, l\right)} \quad (71.11)$$

To evaluate the inverse of this equation, we note that the terms due to the pole at the origin cancel. Hence the only poles needing consideration result from the equation

$$\left.\begin{aligned} \coth \sqrt{\frac{s}{a}}\, l &= -\frac{1}{h}\sqrt{\frac{s}{a}} \\ \cot i \sqrt{\frac{s}{a}}\, l &= \frac{i}{hl}\sqrt{\frac{s}{a}}\, l \end{aligned}\right\} \quad (71.12)$$

or

If we let $\lambda = i\sqrt{s/a}\, l$, it is necessary to determine the roots of the equation,

$$\cot \lambda = \frac{\lambda}{hl} \quad (71.13)$$

shown in Fig. 109.

We need next the term

$$\frac{d}{ds}\left(\frac{1}{h}\sqrt{\frac{s}{a}} \sinh \sqrt{\frac{s}{a}}\, l + \cosh \sqrt{\frac{s}{a}}\, l\right)$$

$$= \frac{l}{2\sqrt{sa}}\left[\frac{1}{h}\sqrt{\frac{s}{a}} \cosh \sqrt{\frac{s}{a}}\, l + \left(\frac{1}{hl} + 1\right) \sinh \sqrt{\frac{s}{a}}\, l\right] \quad (71.14)$$

Expressing $\cosh \sqrt{s/a}\, l$ in terms of $-1/h \sqrt{s/a} \sinh \sqrt{s/a}\, l$ from

Eq. (71.12) and changing to trigonometric functions, we obtain

$$s \frac{d}{ds} \left(\frac{1}{h} \sqrt{\frac{s}{a}} \sinh \sqrt{\frac{s}{a}} \, l + \cosh \sqrt{\frac{s}{a}} \, l \right)$$

$$= - \frac{\lambda^2}{2} \left[\left(1 + \frac{1}{hl} \right) \frac{1}{\lambda} + \frac{\lambda}{(hl)^2} \right] \sin \lambda \quad (71.15)$$

The solution then becomes

$$U(x,t) = 2U_0 \sum_{n=1}^{\infty} \frac{e^{-\frac{\lambda_n^2 at}{l^2}} \cos \lambda_n \frac{x}{l}}{\lambda_n^2 \left[\left(1 + \frac{1}{hl} \right) \frac{1}{\lambda_n} + \frac{\lambda_n}{(hl)^2} \right] \sin \lambda_n}$$

$$= 2U_0 \sum_{n=1}^{\infty} \frac{e^{-\frac{\lambda_n^2 at}{l^2}} \sin \lambda_n}{\lambda_n + \sin \lambda_n \cos \lambda_n} \cos \lambda_n \frac{x}{l} \quad (71.16)$$

In this result, it is evident from Fig. 109 that the λ_n depend only on the quantity hl, which is known as the *Biot's modulus B*.

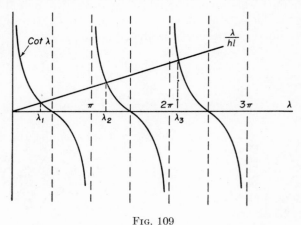

FIG. 109

The other quantity of interest is at/l^2, which is known as the *Fourier modulus F*. The solution at any point x is then a function of B and F, of which the latter can be plotted in various ways.*

$$U(x,t) = f(B,F) \quad (71.17)$$

* L. M. K. Boetter, *Heat Transfer Notes*, Univ. of Calif. Press, 1949.

72. Cooling of a Cylinder. Consider the problem of determining the temperature distribution of a solid circular cylinder, initially at a uniform temperature and cooled in a medium of zero temperature. If the cylinder is long compared to its diameter, the end effects may be ignored and the temperature becomes a function only of the radius and time. The equation of conduction in cylindrical coordinates then becomes

$$\frac{\partial U(r,t)}{\partial t} = a\left[\frac{\partial^2 U(r,t)}{\partial r^2} + \frac{1}{r}\frac{\partial U(r,t)}{\partial r}\right] \tag{72.1}$$

The boundary conditions are as follows:

(1) Initial temperature is uniform and is equal to U_0.

(2) Because of symmetry, the temperature gradient at $r = 0$ is zero:

$$\frac{\partial U(0,t)}{\partial r} = 0, \quad \frac{\partial \overline{U}(0,s)}{\partial r} = 0$$

(3) The rate of heat flow at the cylinder surface $r = R$ follows Newton's law of cooling:

$$\frac{\partial U(R,t)}{\partial r} = -hU(R,t), \quad \frac{\partial \overline{U}(R,s)}{\partial r} = -h\overline{U}(R,s)$$

The transform of Eq. (72.1) is

$$\frac{\partial^2 \overline{U}(r,s)}{\partial r^2} + \frac{1}{r}\frac{\partial \overline{U}(r,s)}{\partial r} - \frac{s}{a}\left[\overline{U}(r,s) - \frac{U_0}{s}\right] = 0 \tag{72.2}$$

If we let

$$\bar{y}(r,s) = \overline{U}(r,s) - \frac{U_0}{s} \tag{72.3}$$

Eq. (72.2) takes the form

$$\frac{\partial^2 \bar{y}(r,s)}{\partial r^2} + \frac{1}{r}\frac{\partial \bar{y}(r,s)}{\partial r} - \frac{s}{a}\bar{y}(r,s) = 0 \tag{72.4}$$

which is recognized as Bessel's equation of zero order and argument $ir\sqrt{s/a}$. Thus a solution which is finite at $r = 0$ is

$$\bar{y}(r,s) = AJ_0\left(ir\sqrt{\frac{s}{a}}\right) \tag{72.5}$$

We notice here that Eq. (72.5) automatically satisfies boundary condition (2). The constant A can be evaluated from boundary condition (3).

$$A \left[\frac{\partial J_0 \left(ir \sqrt{\frac{s}{a}} \right)}{\partial r} \right]_{r=R} = -h \left[A J_0 \left(ir \sqrt{\frac{s}{a}} \right) + \frac{U_0}{s} \right]_{r=R}$$

Since
$$\frac{\partial J_0(kr)}{\partial r} = -k J_1(kr)$$

A becomes

$$A = \frac{-U_0}{s \left[J_0 \left(iR \sqrt{\frac{s}{a}} \right) - \frac{i}{h} \sqrt{\frac{s}{a}} J_1 \left(iR \sqrt{\frac{s}{a}} \right) \right]} \tag{72.6}$$

and the subsidiary solution is established as

$$\bar{U}(r,s) = \frac{U_0}{s} - \frac{U_0 J_0 \left(ir \sqrt{\frac{s}{a}} \right)}{s \left[J_0 \left(iR \sqrt{\frac{s}{a}} \right) - \frac{i}{h} \sqrt{\frac{s}{a}} J_1 \left(iR \sqrt{\frac{s}{a}} \right) \right]} \tag{72.7}$$

To evaluate the inverse of this equation, we note that we have a simple pole at the origin and simple poles at the roots of the equation:

$$J_0 \left(iR \sqrt{\frac{s}{a}} \right) - \frac{i}{h} \sqrt{\frac{s}{a}} J_1 \left(iR \sqrt{\frac{s}{a}} \right) = 0 \tag{72.8}$$

Rewriting this equation in the form

$$J_0(\lambda) - \frac{\lambda}{hR} J_1(\lambda) = 0 \tag{72.9}$$

where $\lambda = iR \sqrt{s/a}$, we see that the roots are

$$iR \sqrt{\frac{s}{a}} = \lambda_1, \lambda_2, \cdots \lambda_n,$$

$$s_n = -\frac{\lambda_n^2 a}{R^2} \tag{72.10}$$

Since $J_0(0) = 1$ and $J_1(0) = 0$, the residue at $s = 0$ is zero. For the residues at the other poles we need the quantity

$$s \frac{d}{ds} \left[J_0 \left(iR \sqrt{\frac{s}{a}} \right) - \frac{i}{h} \sqrt{\frac{s}{a}} J_1 \left(iR \sqrt{\frac{s}{a}} \right) \right]_{s=s_n} \qquad (72.11)$$

$$= s \left[\frac{iR}{2\sqrt{sa}} J_0' \left(iR \sqrt{\frac{s}{a}} \right) - \frac{i}{h} \sqrt{\frac{s}{a}} \frac{iR}{2\sqrt{sa}} J_1' \left(iR \sqrt{\frac{s}{a}} \right) \right.$$

$$\left. - \frac{i}{2h\sqrt{sa}} J_1 \left(iR \sqrt{\frac{s}{a}} \right) \right]$$

By use of the recurrence formula

$$J_1'(\lambda) = J_0(\lambda) - \frac{1}{\lambda} J_1(\lambda)$$

$$J_0'(\lambda) = - J_1(\lambda)$$

Eq. (72.11) becomes

$$\frac{\lambda}{2} \left\{ -J_1(\lambda) - \frac{\lambda}{hR} \left[J_0(\lambda) - \frac{1}{\lambda} J_1(\lambda) \right] - \frac{1}{hR} J_1(\lambda) \right\}_{\lambda=\lambda_n}$$

$$= - \frac{1}{2} \left[\lambda_n J_1(\lambda_n) + \frac{\lambda_n^2}{hR} J_0(\lambda_n) \right]$$

$$= - \frac{1}{2(hR)} [(hR)^2 + \lambda_n^2] J_0(\lambda_n) \qquad (72.12)$$

where J_1 has been replaced by J_0 from Eq. (72.9). With this result, the solution becomes

$$U(r,t) = 2U_0 hR \sum_{n=1}^{\infty} \frac{e^{-\lambda_n \frac{at}{R^2}} J_0 \left(\frac{r}{R} \lambda_n \right)}{[(hR)^2 + \lambda_n^2] J_0(\lambda_n)} \qquad (72.13)$$

Here again $hR = B$ is Biot's modulus and $at/R^2 = F$ is the Fourier modulus. Also, λ_n as determined from Eq. (72.9) is a function only of B. It is evident, then, that the solution is a function only of B and F and can be plotted up in the form

$$U(r,t) = f(B,F) \qquad (72.14)$$

For large values of F, the series given by Eq. (72.13) converges rapidly, and the equations for the temperature at the center and at $r = R$ become

$$U(0,t) \simeq \frac{2U_0 B\, e^{-\lambda_1^2 F}}{(B^2 + \lambda_1^2) J_0(\lambda_1)} \qquad (72.15)$$

$$U(R,t) \simeq \frac{2U_0 B\, e^{-\lambda_1^2 F}}{(B^2 + \lambda_1^2)} \qquad (72.16)$$

Thus the ratio of the temperatures at $r = R$ and $r = 0$ is

$$\frac{U(R,t)}{U(0,t)} = J_0(\lambda_1) \tag{72.17}$$

Also, by considering two different times for which Eq. (72.16) is valid, we obtain a simple formula from which the thermal diffusivity can be computed:*

$$a = \frac{R^2}{\lambda_1^2(t_2 - t_1)} \ln \frac{U(R,t_1)}{U(R,t_2)} \tag{72.18}$$

References

1. Carslaw and Jaeger: *Conduction of Heat in Solids*, Clarendon Press, Oxford, 1947.
2. Boelter, L. M. K.: *Heat Transfer Notes*, Univ. of Calif. Press, 1949.

Problems

164. The face $x = 0$ of a semi-infinite block of uniform temperature U_0 is suddenly exposed to a cold medium of zero temperature. If the surface $x = 0$ obeys Newton's law of cooling,

$$\frac{\partial U(0,t)}{\partial x} = hU(0,t)$$

show that the subsidiary equation is

$$\bar{U}(x,s) = \frac{U_0}{s} \left(1 - \frac{h}{h + \sqrt{\dfrac{s}{a}}} e^{-x\sqrt{\frac{s}{a}}} \right)$$

165. In Prob. 164, let

$$V(x,t) = U(x,t) - \frac{1}{h} \frac{\partial U(x,t)}{\partial x}$$

Then the conduction equation $\partial U/\partial t = a(\partial^2 U/\partial x^2)$ becomes

$$\frac{\partial V}{\partial t} = a \frac{\partial^2 V}{\partial x^2}$$

and the boundary conditions for the problem reduce to

$$V(x,0) = U_0$$
$$V(0,t) = 0$$

* W. T. Thomson, "A Method of Measuring Thermal Diffusivity and Conductivity of Stone and Concrete," *American Society of Testing Materials*, **40** (1940), pages 1073–1081.

Show that the solution for $V(x,t)$ is

$$V(x,t) = U_0 \operatorname{erf}\left(\frac{x}{2\sqrt{at}}\right)$$

and that the equation for the surface temperature is

$$U(0,t) = U_0\, e^{h^2 at}\, \operatorname{erf}\,(h\,\sqrt{at})$$

166. If heat is added at a constant rate q_0 to the face $x = 0$ of a semi-infinite block whose temperature distribution is initially constant, show that the subsidiary equations for the temperature and its inversion are

$$\overline{U}(x,s) = \frac{q_0}{ks}\sqrt{\frac{a}{s}}\, e^{-x\sqrt{\frac{s}{a}}}$$

$$U(x,t) = \frac{q_0}{k}\left[2\sqrt{\frac{at}{\pi}}\, e^{-\frac{x^2}{4at}} - x\operatorname{erfc}\left(\frac{x}{2\sqrt{at}}\right)\right]$$

167. If the slab of Fig. 108 is submerged in a well-stirred liquid, we can assume the temperature of the surface to be zero for $t > 0$; that is. $h = \infty$. If the initial temperature of the slab is uniform and equal to U_0. determine the temperature distribution.

168. If the surface $r = R$ of an infinite circular cylinder of uniform temperature is suddenly cooled to zero temperature, determine its temperature distribution.

169. Steam of temperature U_0 is suddenly introduced in a pipe of inner and outer radius R_1 and R_2, respectively. Assuming the temperature of the inner and outer surfaces to be U_0 and 0 for $t > 0$, determine the temperature distribution.

170. When isothermal surfaces are concentric spheres, the temperature is a function only of r and t, and the equation of heat conduction becomes

$$\frac{\partial U(r,t)}{\partial t} = a\left[\frac{\partial^2 U(r,t)}{\partial r^2} + \frac{2}{r}\frac{\partial U(r,t)}{\partial r}\right]$$

On letting $U = V/r$, this equation reduces to

$$\frac{\partial V(r,t)}{\partial t} = a\frac{\partial^2 V(r,t)}{\partial r^2}$$

Determine the subsidiary form for each of these equations.

171. A sphere of uniform initial temperature U_0 and radius R is subjected to a condition where the surface temperature becomes zero for

$t > 0$. Show that the subsidiary solution is

$$\bar{U}(r,s) = U_0 \left(\frac{1}{s} - \frac{R}{rs} \frac{\sinh rs}{\sinh Rs} \right)$$

Show that the inverse of this equation is

$$U(r,t) = U_0 \left[1 - \frac{R}{\sqrt{\pi at}} \sum_{n=0}^{\infty} e^{-\frac{(2n+1)^2 R^2}{4at}} \right]$$

73. Transmission Lines. The differential equation for the four-parameter transmission line is

$$\frac{\partial E}{\partial x} = -RI - L \frac{\partial I}{\partial t}$$
$$\frac{\partial I}{\partial x} = -GE - C \frac{\partial E}{\partial t} \tag{73.1}$$

where

R = resistance per unit length,
L = inductance per unit length,
G = conductance per unit length,
C = capacitance per unit length.

If we assume that there is no current or voltage in the line prior to $t = 0$, the transformed equations can be reduced to the form

$$\frac{\partial^2 \bar{E}(x,s)}{\partial x^2} = a^2 \bar{E}(x,s)$$
$$\frac{\partial^2 \bar{I}(x,s)}{\partial x^2} = a^2 \bar{I}(x,s) \tag{73.2}$$

where $\qquad a^2 = (G + Cs)(R + Ls) \tag{73.3}$

The general solution for the subsidiary quantities is

$$\bar{E}(x,s) = A_1 e^{-ax} + A_2 e^{ax} \left. \right\}$$
$$\bar{I}(x,s) = A_3 e^{-ax} + A_4 e^{ax} \left. \right\} \tag{73.4}$$

where the A's are functions of s and are to be evaluated from the terminal conditions of the line. The solution for the general case where all four parameters are retained is rather difficult. However, the following four cases are of interest:

(1) $\qquad R = G = 0 \quad a = s\sqrt{LC}$

(2) $\qquad RC = LG \quad a = \sqrt{LC}\left(s + \dfrac{R}{L}\right)$

(3) $\qquad G = L = 0 \quad a = \sqrt{RC}\sqrt{s}$

(4) $\qquad L = 0 \quad a = \sqrt{RC}\sqrt{\left(s + \dfrac{G}{C}\right)}$

Transmission in an Infinite Line. In order for E and I to be finite in an infinite line, A_2 and A_4 of Eq. (73.4) must be zero, and the subsidiary equation reduces to

$$\left.\begin{array}{l} \bar{E}(x,s) = A_1\,e^{-ax} \\ \bar{I}(x,s) = A_3\,e^{-ax} \end{array}\right\} \qquad (73.5)$$

Letting the voltage and current at the sending end $x = 0$ be $E_0(t)$ and $I_0(t)$, we find from Eq. (73.5) that

$$A_1 = \bar{E}_0(s)$$
$$A_3 = \bar{I}_0(s)$$

and
$$\left.\begin{array}{l} \bar{E}(x,s) = \bar{E}_0(s)\,e^{-ax} \\ \bar{I}(x,s) = \bar{I}_0(s)\,e^{-ax} \end{array}\right\} \qquad (73.6)$$

We shall now consider three of the four special cases mentioned previously.

(1) $a = s\sqrt{LC}$.   Substitution of a into Eq. (73.6) results in the following:

$$\left.\begin{array}{l} \bar{E}(x,s) = \bar{E}_0(s)\,e^{-sx\sqrt{LC}} \\ \bar{I}(x,s) = \bar{I}_0(s)\,e^{-sx\sqrt{LC}} \end{array}\right\} \qquad (73.7)$$

Applying the second shifting theorem, we arrive at the solution

$$\left.\begin{array}{l} E(x,t) = E_0(t - x\sqrt{LC})\,\mathfrak{u}(t - x\sqrt{LC}) \\ I(x,t) = I_0(t - x\sqrt{LC})\,\mathfrak{u}(t - x\sqrt{LC}) \end{array}\right\} \qquad (73.8)$$

which indicates that both the voltage and the current are propagated without distortion or attenuation with a velocity equal to $1/\sqrt{LC}$.

(2) $a = \sqrt{LC}\,(s - R/L)$.   Since the exponential can be written in the form

$$e^{-ax} = e^{-\frac{R}{L}x\sqrt{LC}}\,e^{-sx\sqrt{LC}} \qquad (73.9)$$

the solution becomes

$$E(x,t) = e^{-\frac{R}{L}x\sqrt{LC}} E_0(t - x\sqrt{LC})\,\mathfrak{u}(t - x\sqrt{LC}) \left.\vphantom{\begin{matrix}a\\a\end{matrix}}\right\} \quad (73.10)$$
$$I(x,t) = e^{-\frac{R}{L}x\sqrt{LC}} I_0(t - x\sqrt{LC})\,\mathfrak{u}(t - x\sqrt{LC})$$

These equations indicate that there is attenuation along the line but that the wave form is maintained and propagated with a velocity equal to $1/\sqrt{LC}$.

(3) $a = \sqrt{RC}\sqrt{s}$. The subsidiary equation for the voltage for this case is

$$\bar{E}(x,s) = E_0(s)\, e^{-x\sqrt{RC}\sqrt{s}} \quad (73.11)$$

From formula 44, Appendix H, the inverse of the exponential is

$$\mathcal{L}^{-1} e^{-x\sqrt{RC}\sqrt{s}} = \frac{x\sqrt{RC}}{2\sqrt{\pi t^3}}\, e^{-\frac{x^2 RC}{4t}} \quad (73.12)$$

Thus the solution can be expressed by the convolution integral as

$$E(x,t) = \frac{x\sqrt{RC}}{2\sqrt{\pi}} \int_0^t \frac{e^{-\frac{x^2 RC}{4\tau}}}{\sqrt{\tau^3}}\, E_0(t - \tau)\, d\tau \quad (73.13)$$

This equation is not capable of simple interpretation. However, for $E_0 = $ constant the subsidiary equation will have the form

$$\frac{e^{-k\sqrt{s}}}{s}$$

which will result in an error function.

Problems

172. Show that if a steady voltage E_0 is applied to an infinite line with $L = G = 0$, the voltage and current at any point x are

$$E(x,t) = E_0\, \text{erfc}\left(\frac{x}{2}\sqrt{\frac{RC}{t}}\right)$$
$$I(x,t) = E_0\sqrt{\frac{C}{\pi Rt}}\, e^{-\frac{x^2 RC}{4t}}$$

173. A line of length l with $L = G = 0$ is open-circuited at the far end. If a constant voltage E_0 is applied to the sending end, determine the voltage and current.

$$\bar{E}(x,s) = \frac{E_0 \cosh \sqrt{CRs} \,(l - x)}{\cosh \sqrt{CRs} \, l}$$

$$\bar{I}(x,s) = E_0 \sqrt{\frac{C}{Rs}} \frac{\sinh \sqrt{CRs} \,(l - x)}{\cosh \sqrt{CRs} \, l}$$

$$E(x,t) = E_0 \left\{ 1 - \frac{4}{\pi} \sum_{n=1}^{\infty} \frac{1}{n} \sin \frac{n\pi x}{2l} e^{-\frac{n^2\pi^2 t}{4RCl^2}} \right\}$$

$$I(x,t) = \frac{2E_0}{Rl} \sum_{n=1}^{\infty} \cos \frac{n\pi x}{2l} e^{-\frac{n^2\pi^2 t}{4RCl^2}}$$

174. A finite line of length l has $R = G = 0$. If the far end is short-circuited, determine the voltage and current at x due to a steady voltage E_0 at the sending end.

175. A sinusoidal voltage $E_0 \sin \omega t$ is applied to the line of Problem **174.** Determine the natural frequencies of the line when (a) the far end is short-circuited, (b) the far end is open-circuited.

(a)
$$\begin{cases} \bar{E}(x,s) = \dfrac{E_0\omega}{s^2 + \omega^2} \dfrac{\sinh s \sqrt{LC} \,(l - x)}{\sinh s \sqrt{LC} \, l} \\[2ex] \omega_n = \dfrac{k\pi}{l \sqrt{LC}}(k = 1, 2, 3, \cdots) \end{cases}$$

176. Show that for the general case of a finite line of length l, the subsidiary voltage and current are

$$\bar{E}(x,s) = \bar{E}(0,s) \frac{\sinh a(l - x)}{\sinh al} + \bar{E}(l,s) \frac{\sinh ax}{\sinh al}$$

$$\bar{I}(x,s) = \frac{a}{(R + Ls)} \left[\bar{E}(0,s) \frac{\cosh a(l - x)}{\sinh al} - \bar{E}(l,s) \frac{\cosh ax}{\sinh al} \right]$$

74. Vibration of Beams. The differential equation for the transverse vibration of a uniform beam with applied force $f(x,t)$ can be obtained from the loading equation of Section 36 by including the inertia force $-m(\partial^2 y/\partial t^2)$:

$$EI \frac{\partial^4 y(x,t)}{\partial x^4} = -m \frac{\partial^2 y(x,t)}{\partial t^2} + f(x,t) \tag{74.1}$$

If we let the initial displacement and velocity be $u(x)$ and $v(x)$, the transform of Eq. (74.1) with respect to t becomes

$$\frac{d^4\bar{y}(x,s)}{dx^4} + \left(\frac{ms^2}{EI}\right)\bar{y}(x,s) = \frac{m}{EI}[su(x) + v(x)] + \frac{\bar{f}(x,s)}{EI} \quad (74.2)$$

Making the substitution

$$\beta^4 = -\frac{ms^2}{EI} \quad (74.3)$$

$$\bar{\phi}(x,s) = \frac{m}{EI}[su(x) + v(x)] + \frac{\bar{f}(x,s)}{EI} \quad (74.4)$$

we find that Eq. (74.2) reduces to

$$\frac{d^4\bar{y}(x,s)}{dx^4} - \beta^4\bar{y}(x,s) = \bar{\phi}(x,s) \quad (74.5)$$

Taking next the transform with respect to x with p as the subsidiary variable, we have

$$(p^4 - \beta^4)\bar{\bar{y}}(p,s) = \bar{\bar{\phi}}(p,s) + p^3\bar{y}(0,s) + p^2\bar{y}_x'(0,s)$$
$$+ p\bar{y}_x''(0,s) + \bar{y}_x'''(0,s)$$

$$\bar{\bar{y}}(p,s) = \frac{\bar{\bar{\phi}}(p,s)}{p^4 - \beta^4}$$
$$+ \frac{p^3\bar{y}(0,s) + p^2\bar{y}_x'(0,s) + p\bar{y}_x''(0,s) + \bar{y}_x'''(0,s)}{p^4 - \beta^4} \quad (74.6)$$

In this equation, $\bar{y}(0,s)$, $\bar{y}_x'(0,s)$, $\bar{y}_x''(0,s)$, and $\bar{y}_x'''(0,s)$ are the transforms with respect to t of the deflection, slope, $1/EI \times$ moment, and $1/EI \times$ shear at the origin $x = 0$.

Carrying out the inversion first with respect to x, we obtain the equation

$$\bar{y}(x,s) = \frac{1}{2\beta^3}\int_0^x \bar{\phi}(\xi,s)[\sinh\beta(x-\xi) - \sin\beta(x-\xi)]\,d\xi$$

$$+ \frac{1}{2}\bar{y}(0,s)(\cosh\beta x + \cos\beta x) + \frac{1}{2\beta}\bar{y}_x'(0,s)(\sinh\beta x + \sin\beta x)$$

$$+ \frac{1}{2\beta^2}\bar{y}_x''(0,s)(\cosh\beta x - \cos\beta x)$$

$$+ \frac{1}{2\beta^3}\bar{y}_x'''(0,s)(\sinh\beta x - \sin\beta x) \quad (74.7)$$

Before we proceed further with the problem, it is advisable to specify the applied load and the boundary and initial conditions.

EXAMPLE 74.1: A simply supported beam of length l has a concentrated load at $x = a$ which varies in an arbitrary manner with time (see Fig. 110).   If the beam is initially straight and at rest, determine the equation for its deflection.

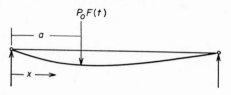

$$P_0 F(t)$$

$$a$$

$$x \longrightarrow$$

FIG. 110

The loading corresponding to a concentrated force is $P_0 \mathfrak{U}'(x - a)$. Thus if $F(t)$ is its time variation, we have

$$f(x,t) = -P_0 \mathfrak{U}'(x - a)F(t) \tag{74.8}$$

$$\bar{\phi}(x,s) = -\frac{P_0 \mathfrak{U}'(x - a)}{EI} \bar{F}(s) \tag{74.9}$$

Since the deflection and moment are zero at $x = 0$, Eq. (74.7) now becomes

$$\bar{y}(x,s) = -\frac{1}{2\beta^3} \int_0^x \frac{P_0 \mathfrak{U}'(\xi - a)\bar{F}(s)}{EI} [\sinh \beta(x - \xi) - \sin \beta(x - \xi)] \, d\xi$$
$$+ C_1 \sinh \beta x + C_2 \sin \beta x \tag{74.10}$$

where

$$C_1 = \frac{1}{2\beta} \bar{y}_x'(0,s) + \frac{1}{2\beta^3} \bar{y}_x'''(0,s)$$

$$C_2 = \frac{1}{2\beta} \bar{y}_x'(0,s) - \frac{1}{2\beta^3} \bar{y}_x'''(0,s)$$

At the end $x = l$, the deflection and moment are also zero, so that we obtain the two equations

$$0 = \frac{-P_0 \bar{F}(s)}{2\beta^3 EI} \int_0^l \mathfrak{U}'(\xi - a)[\sinh \beta(l - \xi) - \sin \beta(l - \xi)] \, d\xi$$
$$+ C_1 \sinh \beta l + C_2 \sin \beta l \tag{74.11}$$

$$0 = \frac{-P_0 \bar{F}(s)}{2\beta^3 EI} \int_0^l \mathfrak{U}'(\xi - a) [\sinh \beta(l - \xi) + \sin \beta(l - \xi)] \, d\xi$$
$$+ C_1 \sinh \beta l - C_2 \sin \beta l \tag{74.12}$$

Solving for the C's,* we obtain

* Note that

$$\int_0^l \mathfrak{U}'(\xi - a)\psi(\xi) \, d\xi = \psi(a)$$

$$C_1 = \frac{P_0 \bar{F}(s) \sinh \beta(l - a)}{2\beta^3 EI \sinh \beta l}$$
$$C_2 = -\frac{P_0 \bar{F}(s) \sin \beta(l - a)}{2\beta^3 EI \sin \beta l}$$

(74.13)

Thus the subsidiary deflection becomes

$$\bar{y}(x,s) = -\frac{P_0 \bar{F}(s)}{2\beta^3 EI} \int_0^x \mathfrak{U}'(\xi - a)[\sinh \beta(x - \xi) - \sin \beta(x - \xi)]\, d\xi$$
$$+ \frac{P_0 \bar{F}(s)}{2\beta^3 EI} \left[\frac{\sinh \beta(l - a) \sinh \beta x \sin \beta l - \sin \beta(l - a) \sin \beta x \sinh \beta l}{\sinh \beta l \sin \beta l} \right]$$
$$= \frac{P_0 \bar{F}(s)}{2\beta^3 EI} \left\{ [\sin \beta(x - a) - \sinh \beta(x - a)]\mathfrak{U}(x - a) \right.$$
$$\left. + \frac{\sinh \beta(l - a) \sinh \beta x \sin \beta l - \sin \beta(l - a) \sin \beta x \sinh \beta l}{\sinh \beta l \sin \beta l} \right\}$$

(74.14)

(1) *Steady-state Solution for Harmonic Time Function.* If $F(t)$ is harmonic, the steady-state solution can be easily found from Eq. (74.14) by letting $s = i\omega$ in all terms except $\bar{F}(s)$, which is replaced by $F(t) = \sin \omega t$ (see Section 24). $y(x,t)$ is then deduced from Eq. (74.14) as*

$$y(x,t) = \frac{P_0 \sin \omega t}{2\beta^3 EI} \left\{ [\sin \beta(x - a) - \sinh \beta(x - a)]\mathfrak{U}(x - a) \right.$$
$$\left. + \frac{\sinh \beta(l - a) \sinh \beta x \sin \beta l - \sin \beta(l - a) \sin \beta x \sinh \beta l}{\sinh \beta l \sin \beta l} \right\}$$

(74.15)

where
$$\beta^4 = \frac{m\omega^2}{EI}$$

(2) *Beam Subjected to an Impulse of Magnitude $\mathfrak{I}_0$ lb-sec.* For an impulse of $\mathfrak{I}_0$ lb-sec concentrated at $x = a$, the loading equation becomes

$$f(x,t) = -\mathfrak{I}_0 \mathfrak{U}'(x - a)\mathfrak{U}'(t)$$

(74.16)

Thus we need only to replace P_0 by $\mathfrak{I}_0$ and $\bar{F}(s)$ by 1, and the deflection for $x < a$ from Eq. (74.14) becomes

$$\bar{y}(x,s) = \frac{\mathfrak{I}_0}{2EI} \left[\frac{\sinh \beta(l - a) \sinh \beta x \sin \beta l - \sin \beta(l - a) \sin \beta x \sinh \beta l}{\beta^3 \sinh \beta l \sin \beta l} \right]$$

(74.17)

* W. T. Thomson, "The Laplace Transform Solution of Beams," *Jour. Acoustical Soc. of Amer.*, **21**, 1 (1949), pages 34–38.

where
$$\beta = \sqrt{i\,\frac{s}{h}} \quad \text{and} \quad h = \sqrt{\frac{EI}{m}}$$

The poles of Eq. (74.17) are all simple. It can be easily shown that there is no pole at the origin $s = 0$. Taking the first two terms of the expansion for sinh and sin, we find that the limiting value of the numerator as $\beta \rightarrow 0$ is proportional to β^5, so that the function does not have a pole at the origin. Hence the only poles of Eq. (74.17) are the roots of the equations

$$\sinh \beta l = 0$$
$$\sin \beta l = 0$$

or
$$\left.\begin{array}{ll} \beta = \dfrac{in\pi}{l}, & s_n = i\,\dfrac{n^2\pi^2 h}{l^2} \\[2ex] \beta = \dfrac{n\pi}{l}, & s_n = -\,i\,\dfrac{n^2\pi^2 h}{l^2} \end{array}\right\} (n = 1, 2, 3, \cdots) \quad (74.18)$$

For the residues we shall need the quantity

$$\frac{d}{d\beta}\,(\beta^3 \sinh \beta l \sin \beta l)\,\frac{d\beta}{ds} = i\,\frac{\beta^2 l}{2h}\,(\sin \beta l \cosh \beta l + \sinh \beta l \cos \beta l)_{s=s_n}$$
$$(74.19)$$

Substituting Eq. (74.18) into the expression for the residues,

$$\frac{2h[\sinh \beta(l-a) \sinh \beta x \sin \beta l - \sin \beta(l-a) \sin \beta x \sinh \beta l]\,e^{st}}{i\beta^2 l(\sin \beta l \cosh \beta l + \sinh \beta l \cos \beta l)} \quad (74.20)$$

we obtain

$$i\,\frac{2hl}{n^2\pi^2}\,\sin\frac{n\pi x}{l}\,\sin\frac{n\pi a}{l}\,e^{i\frac{n^2\pi^2 ht}{l^2}} \quad \left(\text{for } \beta = \frac{in\pi}{l}\right)$$

$$-i\,\frac{2hl}{n^2\pi^2}\,\sin\frac{n\pi x}{l}\,\sin\frac{n\pi a}{l}\,e^{-i\frac{n^2\pi^2 ht}{l}} \quad \left(\text{for } \beta = \frac{n\pi}{l}\right)$$

Addition of these residues gives the final expression for the deflection:

$$y(x,t) = \frac{-2\mathcal{I}_0 l}{\pi^2 \sqrt{EIm}}\sum_{n=1}^{\infty}\frac{1}{n^2}\,\sin\frac{n\pi x}{l}\,\sin\frac{n\pi a}{l}\,\sin\frac{n^2\pi^2}{l^2}\sqrt{\frac{EI}{m}}\,t \quad (74.21)$$

which is clearly a normal mode solution.

If $a = l/2$, the deflection under the load becomes

$$y\left(\frac{l}{2}, t\right) = \frac{-2g_0 l}{\pi^2 \sqrt{EIm}}\left(\sin \frac{\pi^2 ht}{l^2} - \frac{1}{3^2}\sin 3^2 \frac{\pi^2 ht}{l^2} + \frac{1}{5^2}\sin 5^2\frac{\pi^2 ht}{l^2} - \cdots\right)$$

which converges very rapidly.

Problems

177. From Eq. (74.15) establish the natural frequencies of the simply supported beam to be

$$\omega_n = \frac{k^2\pi^2}{l^2}\sqrt{\frac{EI}{m}} \qquad (k = 1, 2, 3, \cdots)$$

178. A concentrated force P_0 with arbitrary time variation $F(t)$ acts at the end of a cantilever beam of length l which is initially straight and at rest. (a) Determine $\bar{y}(x,s)$. (b) Determine $y(x,t)$ when $F(t) = \sin \omega t$. (c) Establish the natural frequencies of the beam.

$$\bar{y}(x,s) = \frac{-P_0\bar{F}(s)}{\beta^3 EI}\left\{\frac{[\cosh \beta x - \cos \beta x] - [\sinh \beta x - \sin \beta x]}{\left(\dfrac{\sinh \beta l + \sin \beta l}{\cosh \beta l + \cos \beta l}\right) - (\cosh \beta l + \cos \beta l)}\right\}$$

179. The deflection due to an impulse is given by Eq. (74.21). The moment and shear derived from this equation result in a diverging series. This difficulty can be avoided by assuming the time function to be a rectangular pulse of finite magnitude. Establish a solution for this type of function.

180. Determine the solution for Prob. 178 when $F(t) = \mathfrak{U}'(t)$.

181. Determine the subsidiary solution for a simply supported beam when the load is uniformly distributed with x but arbitrary with t.

182. If a concentrated load W moves along a simply supported beam with constant speed v, determine the deflection.

183. Repeat Prob. 182 for the load uniformly distributed over a length b.

CHAPTER 7

Difference Equations

75. Introduction. If a function y is known at equally spaced values of x, then an equation connecting consecutive values of y is called a difference equation. For example, if y for integer values of x is defined by the first two columns of the following table, the first, second, and third differences, designated by Δy_x, $\Delta^2 y_x$ and $\Delta^3 y_x$,

x	y_x	Δy_x	$\Delta^2 y_x$	$\Delta^3 y_x$
0	1			
1	3	2	1	
2	6	3	1	0
3	10	4	1	0
4	15	5		

can be expressed by the equations

$$\left.\begin{aligned}
\Delta y_x &= y_{x+1} - y_x = 2 + x \\
\Delta^2 y_x &= \Delta(\Delta y_x) = \Delta y_{x+1} - \Delta y_x = y_{x+2} - 2y_{x+1} + y_x = 1 \\
\Delta^3 y_x &= \Delta(\Delta^2 y_x) = \Delta^2 y_{x+1} - \Delta^2 y_x = y_{x+3} - 3y_{x+2} \\
&\qquad\qquad\qquad\qquad\qquad\qquad + 3y_{x+1} - y_x = 0
\end{aligned}\right\} \quad (75.1)$$

These represent first-, second-, and third-order difference equations satisfying the values of y_x in the above table for integer values of x.

The most important applications of difference equations arise in the electrical or mechanical systems where there is a recurrence of identical sections. Electrical wave filters, multistage amplifiers, insulator strings, continuous beams of equal span, crankshafts of multicylinder engines, and acoustical filters are examples of systems with recurrence of identical sections. The usual method of solving such systems is generally lengthy when the number of elements is large, whereas the method of difference equations reduces the labor and complexities of the solution.

We shall discuss only difference equations of first and second order, since the procedure can be extended to equations of higher

163

order.   The general form of the second-order equation is

$$ay_x + by_{x+1} + cy_{x+2} = f_x \qquad (75.2)$$

where a, b, and c are constants and f_x is the value of the right side
of the equation at x.   The solution y_x is a set of numbers depending
on the value of x which satisfy the above equation and the boundary
conditions at the ends $x = 0$ and n.

76. Solution by Laplace Transformation.   To make the problem
suitable to an operational approach, we introduce in place of the
numbers y_x the *jump function* $y(x)$ shown in Fig. 111.   Such a

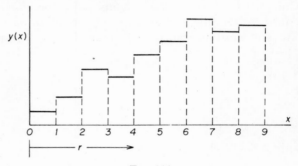

Fɪɢ. 111

function can be expressed mathematically in terms of the unit
function as

$$y(x) = \sum_{r=0}^{\infty} y_r[\mathfrak{u}(x - r) - \mathfrak{u}(x - r - 1)] \qquad (76.1)$$

which represents a sum of a series of rectangles of unit base and
height y_r.   The function $y(x + 1)$ then represents the same curve
shifted to the left through a distance $x = 1$.   Thus the difference
$y(x + 1) - y(x)$ at any value of x is numerically equal to the
difference in the numbers $y_{x+1} - y_x$.   We see then that Eq. (75.2)
can be written in terms of the jump function as

$$ay(x) + by(x + 1) + cy(x + 2) = f(x) \qquad (76.2)$$

which holds for all values of x.   For example, if $x = r + e$ where e
is a fraction less than 1, then $y(r + e) = y_r$.

To solve this equation operationally, we first define the Laplace transform of the jump function as

$$\mathcal{L}y(x) = \int_0^\infty e^{-sx}\, y(x)\, dx = \bar{y}(s) \qquad (76.3)$$

Since each term of $y(x)$ is a constant y_r multiplied by a unit pulse $[\mathcal{u}(x - r) - \mathcal{u}(x - r - 1)]$, the value of this transform is readily seen to be

$$\bar{y}(s) = \sum_{r=0}^\infty y_r \left[\frac{e^{-rs}}{s} - \frac{e^{-(r+1)s}}{s} \right]$$

$$= \frac{(1 - e^{-s})}{s} \sum_{r=0}^\infty y_r\, e^{-rs} \qquad (76.4)$$

To obtain the transform of $y(x + 1)$, we write

$$\mathcal{L}(y + 1) = \int_0^\infty e^{-sx}\, y(x + 1)\, dx \qquad (76.5)$$

and let $(x + 1) = \lambda$.

$$\mathcal{L}y(x + 1) = e^s \int_1^\infty e^{-s\lambda}\, y(\lambda)\, d\lambda$$

$$= e^s \int_0^\infty e^{-s\lambda}\, y(\lambda)\, d\lambda - y_0\, e^s \int_0^1 e^{-s\lambda}\, d\lambda$$

$$= e^s \bar{y}(s) - y_0 \frac{e^s(1 - e^{-s})}{s} \qquad (76.6)$$

In this equation y_0 is the value of $y(x)$ in the interval $x = 0$ to 1. If this procedure is repeated, the transform of $y(x + 2)$ becomes

$$\mathcal{L}y(x + 2) = e^{2s}\, \bar{y}(s) - (y_0\, e^s + y_1) \frac{e^s(1 - e^{-s})}{s} \qquad (76.7)$$

When these expressions are substituted into Eq. (76.2), the subsidiary equation becomes

$$(a + b\, e^s + c\, e^{2s})\bar{y}(s) = \bar{f}(s) + [y_0(b + c\, e^s) + y_1 c] \frac{e^s(1 - e^{-s})}{s} \qquad (76.8)$$

The inverse transform of $\bar{y}(s)$ fitted to the boundary conditions then results in the final solution.

77. Transforms of Commonly Encountered Jump Functions. In Eq. (76.2) $f(x)$ is also a jump function, and hence it is convenient to have at our disposal the transforms of the more frequently encountered jump functions. Such a table will also be an aid in determining the inverse transformation. It is evident from Eq. (76.4) that the quantity $(1 - e^{-s})/s$ will be a factor in all types of jump functions.

(1) *Transform of a Constant* $y(x) = c$. Using Eq. (76.4) with $y_r = c$, we obtain

$$\mathcal{L}c = \frac{(1 - e^{-s})}{s} \sum_{r=0}^{\infty} c\, e^{-rs} = \frac{(1 - e^{-s})}{s} \frac{c}{(1 - e^{-s})} = \frac{c}{s} \quad (77.1)$$

which agrees with our previous result for the Laplace transform

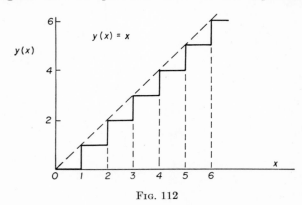

Fig. 112

of a constant. It is, however, convenient in many cases to retain the factor $(1 - e^{-s})/s$.

(2) *Transform of the Jump Function* $y(x) = x$ (*see Fig.* 112). From Eq. (76.4) we have

$$\mathcal{L}x = \frac{(1 - e^{-s})}{s} \sum_{r=0}^{\infty} r\, e^{-rs} = \frac{(1 - e^{-s})}{s} [e^{-s}(1 + 2e^{-s} + 3e^{-2s} + \cdots)]$$

$$= \frac{(1 - e^{-s})}{s} \frac{e^{-s}}{(1 - e^{-s})^2} \quad (77.2)$$

Multiplying and dividing by e^{2s}, we obtain

$$\mathcal{L}x = \frac{(1 - e^{-s})}{s} \frac{e^{s}}{(e^{s} - 1)^2} \quad (77.3)$$

(3) *Transform of the First Difference.*   The Laplace transform of the first difference can be obtained from Eq. (76.6) as

$$\mathcal{L}\,\Delta y(x) = \mathcal{L}[y(x+1) - y(x)]$$

$$= (e^s - 1)\bar{y}(s) - y_0\,e^{-s}\,\frac{(1 - e^{-s})}{s} \qquad (77.4)$$

The use of this equation is illustrated by the following problems.

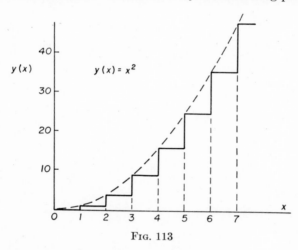

FIG. 113

(4) *Transform of the Jump Function* $y(x) = x^2$ *(see Fig. 113).* The first difference is

$$\Delta y(x) = (x + 1)^2 - x^2 = 2x + 1 \qquad (77.5)$$

Taking the transform of each side of the equation, we have, from Eqs. (77.4), (77.3), and (77.1),

$$(e^s - 1)\mathcal{L}x^2 = \frac{e^s(1 - e^{-s})}{s}\left\{\frac{2}{(e^s - 1)^2} + \frac{1}{e^s(1 - e^{-s})}\right\}$$

$$= \frac{e^s(1 - e^{-s})}{s}\left\{\frac{2 + (e^s - 1)}{(e^s - 1)^2}\right\}$$

$$\mathcal{L}x^2 = \frac{e^s(1 - e^{-s})}{s}\left\{\frac{e^s + 1}{(e^s - 1)^3}\right\} \qquad (77.6)$$

(5) *Transform of the Jump Function* $\sinh \beta x$ *and* $\cosh \beta x$.   Here the following equations form the first difference:

$$\Delta \sinh \beta x = \sinh \beta(x + 1) - \sinh \beta x$$
$$= (\cosh \beta - 1) \sinh \beta x + \sinh \beta \cosh \beta x \quad (77.7)$$

$$\Delta \cosh \beta x = \cosh \beta(x + 1) - \cosh \beta x$$
$$= (\cosh \beta - 1) \cosh \beta x + \sinh \beta \sinh \beta x \quad (77.8)$$

Using (3) for the transform of the first difference, we obtain

$$(e^s - 1)\mathcal{L} \sinh \beta x = (\cosh \beta - 1)\mathcal{L} \sinh \beta x + \sinh \beta \mathcal{L} \cosh \beta x \quad (77.9)$$

$$(e^s - 1)\mathcal{L} \cosh \beta x - \frac{e^s(1 - e^{-s})}{s}$$
$$= (\cosh \beta - 1)\mathcal{L} \cosh \beta x + \sinh \beta \mathcal{L} \sinh \beta x \quad (77.10)$$

Collecting coefficients of like terms, we have

$$(e^s - \cosh \beta)\mathcal{L} \sinh \beta x = \sinh \beta \mathcal{L} \cosh \beta x$$

$$(e^s - \cosh \beta)\mathcal{L} \cosh \beta x = \frac{e^s(1 - e^{-s})}{s} + \sinh \beta \mathcal{L} \sinh \beta x$$

Finally, we solve these two equations for $\mathcal{L} \sinh \beta x$ and $\mathcal{L} \cosh \beta x$:

$$\mathcal{L} \sinh \beta x = \left\{ \frac{\sinh \beta}{e^{2s} - 2e^s \cosh \beta + 1} \right\} \frac{e^s(1 - e^{-s})}{s} \quad (77.11)$$

$$\mathcal{L} \cosh \beta x = \left\{ \frac{e^s - \cosh \beta}{e^{2s} - 2e^s \cosh \beta + 1} \right\} \frac{e^s(1 - e^{-s})}{s} \quad (77.12)$$

(6) *Transform of the Jump Function* $y(x) = c^x$. Forming the first difference, we have

$$\Delta c^x = c^{x+1} - c^x = (c - 1)c^x \quad (77.13)$$

Applying (3), we get

$$(e^s - 1)\mathcal{L}c^x - \frac{e^s(1 - e^{-s})}{s} = (c - 1)\mathcal{L}c^x$$

$$\mathcal{L}c^x = \frac{e^s(1 - e^{-s})}{(e^s - c)s} \quad (77.14)$$

References

1. Gardner, F. M., and Barnes, J. L., *Transients in Linear Systems*, John Wiley, 1942, Chapter 9.

2. Carslaw, H. S., and Jaeger, J. C., *Operational Methods in Applied Mathematics*, Oxford Univ. Press, 1947 (2nd Ed.), pages 316–320.

3. Churchill, R. V., *Modern Operational Mathematics in Engineering*, McGraw-Hill, 1944, pages 23–28.

Problems

184. Determine the Laplace transform of the jump function $f(x) = x$ by considering $f(x)$ to be a series of unit step functions started at $x = 1, 2, 3, \cdots$; that is, $f(x) = \mathfrak{U}(x - 1) + \mathfrak{U}(x - 2) + \mathfrak{U}(x - 3) + \cdots$.

185. Determine the Laplace transform of the jump function $f(x) = x$ by taking the transform of its first difference.

186. Determine the Laplace transform of the jump functions $\sin \beta x$ and $\cos \beta x$.

78. The Multicylinder Engine. The torsional oscillations of a multicylinder engine are generally studied from the approximate system of Fig. 114, where the moment of inertia J is lumped at each cylinder and connected by a massless shaft of stiffness k.

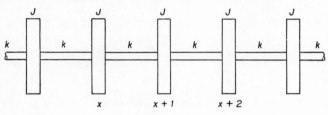

FIG. 114

Writing the torque equation for the $x + 1$ disk and assuming the oscillation to be harmonic, we have

$$-J\omega^2\theta(x + 1) = k[\theta(x + 2) - \theta(x + 1)] - k[\theta(x + 1) - \theta(x)] \quad (78.1)$$

On rearranging, we recognize the equation to be a homogeneous difference equation of second order:

$$\theta(x) - 2\left(1 - \frac{J\omega^2}{2k}\right)\theta(x + 1) + \theta(x + 2) = 0 \quad (78.2)$$

To solve this equation operationally, we apply the Laplace transformation, keeping in mind that $\theta(x)$ is a jump function. By Eqs. (76.6) and (76.7), the subsidiary equation becomes

$$\bar{\theta}(s) = \frac{\left[-2\left(1 - \dfrac{J\omega^2}{2k}\right)\theta(0) + e^s\,\theta(0) + \theta(1)\right](1 - e^{-s})e^s}{e^{2s} - 2\left(1 - \dfrac{J\omega^2}{2k}\right)e^s + 1} \quad (78.3)$$

Making the substitution

$$\cosh \beta = \left(1 - \frac{J\omega^2}{2k}\right)$$

we find the inverse from Eqs. (77.11) and (77.12) as

$$\theta(x) = \theta(0)\left(\cosh \beta x - \frac{\cosh \beta}{\sinh \beta} \sinh \beta x\right) + \theta(1)\frac{\sinh \beta x}{\sinh \beta} \quad (78.4)$$

To complete the solution, we need to specify the boundary conditions at each end.

79. Natural Frequencies of n Disks. To determine the natural frequencies of n disks, we refer to Fig. 115, where the shaft is

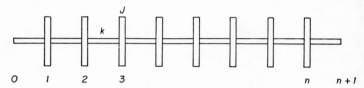

FIG. 115

assumed to extend beyond the first and nth disks to stations 0 and $n + 1$, respectively. Since there is no disk at $x = 0$ and $n + 1$, there can be no twist in the end shafts. Thus the boundary equations become

$$\begin{rcases} \theta(0) = \theta(1) \\ \theta(n) = \theta(n + 1) \end{rcases} \quad (79.1)$$

Applying the first of these to Eq. (78.4), we obtain

$$\theta(x) = \theta(1)\left[\cosh \beta x + (1 - \cosh \beta)\frac{\sinh \beta x}{\sinh \beta}\right] \quad (79.2)$$

Letting $x = n$ and $n + 1$ and substituting into the second boundary equation, we obtain

$$\cosh n\beta + (1 - \cosh \beta)\frac{\sinh n\beta}{\sinh \beta} = \cosh (n + 1)\beta$$

$$+ (1 - \cosh \beta)\frac{\sinh (n + 1)\beta}{\sinh \beta} \quad (79.3)$$

Upon simplification, the above equation reduces to

$$\sinh n\beta(1 - \cosh \beta) = 0 \quad (79.4)$$

which is satisfied if

$$\left. \begin{array}{l} \cosh \beta = 1 \\ \sinh n\beta = 0 \end{array} \right\} \tag{79.5}$$

To interpret these equations, we note that we had originally made the substitution

$$\cosh \beta = \left(1 - \frac{J\dot\omega^2}{2k} \right) \tag{79.6}$$

It is evident from this equation that $\cosh \beta$ must be less than 1. Letting $\beta = \gamma + i\lambda$, where γ and λ are real numbers, we can write

$$\cosh \beta = \cosh (\gamma + i\lambda) = \cosh \gamma \cos \lambda + i \sinh \gamma \sin \lambda$$

If we choose $\gamma = 0$, then

$$\cosh \beta = \cos \lambda$$

which must lie between ± 1. If we were to choose $\lambda = 0$ or $\lambda = \pi$, we should obtain

$$\cosh \beta = \cosh \gamma = \left(1 - \frac{J\omega^2}{2k} \right)$$
$$\cosh \beta = - \cosh \gamma$$

The first is not possible, since $\cosh \gamma$ must be greater than 1. The second is also not possible, since a positive number cannot equal a negative number. Thus we conclude that the only possible choice is $\gamma = 0$ and $\beta = i\lambda$, from which we obtain

$$\cos \lambda = \left(1 - \frac{J\omega^2}{2k} \right) \tag{79.7}$$

$$\omega^2 = \frac{2k}{J} (1 - \cos \lambda) = \frac{4k}{J} \sin^2 \frac{\lambda}{2} \tag{79.8}$$

The values of λ are obtained from Eqs. (79.5) as

$$\cos \lambda = 1 \qquad (\lambda = 0, 2\pi, 4\pi, \cdots)$$
$$\sin n\lambda = 0 \qquad \left(\lambda = 0, \frac{\pi}{n}, \frac{2\pi}{n}, \cdots \frac{r\pi}{n} \cdots \right)$$

The natural frequencies are therefore given by the equation

$$\omega = 2 \sqrt{\frac{k}{J}} \sin \frac{r\pi}{2n}_{r=0,1,2,\cdots n} \tag{79.9}$$

If we go beyond $r = n$, the ω's are repeated, and hence there are only n distinct natural frequencies—a result to be expected for a system with n degrees of freedom. The frequency spectrum corresponding to Eq. (79.9) is conveniently shown by the diagram of Fig. 116.

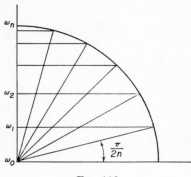

FIG. 116

80. Natural Frequencies with Flywheels or Load. Figure 117 shows an n-cylinder engine coupled to loads or flywheels on each end. To determine the natural frequencies of this system, again we shall assume the shaft between 0 and 1 and n and $n + 1$ to be rigid and massless so that $\theta(0) = \theta(1)$ and $\theta(n) = \theta(n + 1)$.

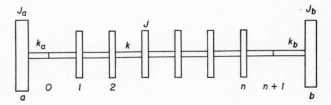

FIG. 117

Considering the left end, we can write two equations

$$-J_a\omega^2\theta(a) = k_a[\theta(1) - \theta(a)] \tag{80.1}$$
$$-J\omega^2\theta(1) = k[\theta(2) - \theta(1)] - k_a[\theta(1) - \theta(a)] \tag{80.2}$$

Eliminating $\theta(a)$ from these two equations and letting

$$K_a = \frac{k_a}{1 - \dfrac{k_a}{J_a\omega^2}} \tag{80.3}$$

we obtain the equation

$$-\frac{K_a}{k}\,\theta(1) - \left(1 - \frac{J\omega^2}{k}\right)\theta(1) + \theta(2) = 0 \tag{80.4}$$

If we compare this equation with the original difference equation for $x = 0$,

$$\theta(0) - 2\left(1 - \frac{J\omega^2}{2k}\right)\theta(1) + \theta(2) = 0 \qquad (80.5)$$

we find that

$$\theta(0) - \theta(1) = -\frac{K_a}{k}\theta(1)$$

or
$$\theta(0) = \left(1 - \frac{K_a}{k}\right)\theta(1) \qquad (80.6)$$

It is evident then that a similar equation can also be obtained for the right end:

$$\theta(n + 1) = \left(1 - \frac{K_b}{k}\right)\theta(n) \qquad (80.7)$$

Equations (80.6) and (80.7) are now the boundary conditions which the general solution, Eq. (78.4), must satisfy. Substituting Eq. (80.6) into Eq. (78.4), we obtain

$$\theta(x) = \theta(1)\left[\left(\cosh \beta x - \frac{\cosh \beta}{\sinh \beta}\sinh \beta x\right)\left(1 - \frac{K_a}{k}\right) + \frac{\sinh \beta x}{\sinh \beta}\right] \qquad (80.8)$$

Letting $x = n$ and $n + 1$ and substituting into Eq. (80.7), we have

$$\left[\cosh (n + 1)\beta - \frac{\cosh \beta}{\sinh \beta}\sinh (n + 1)\beta\right]\left(1 - \frac{K_a}{k}\right) + \frac{\sinh (n + 1)\beta}{\sinh \beta}$$

$$= \left(1 - \frac{K_b}{k}\right)\left[\left(\cosh n\beta - \frac{\cosh \beta}{\sinh \beta}\sinh n\beta\right)\left(1 - \frac{K_a}{k}\right) + \frac{\sinh n\beta}{\sinh n\beta}\right]$$

which reduces to the form

$$\sinh (n + 1)\beta - \left(2 - \frac{K_a + K_b}{k}\right)\sinh n\beta$$

$$+ \left(1 - \frac{K_a}{k}\right)\left(1 - \frac{K_b}{k}\right)\sinh (n - 1)\beta = 0 \qquad (80.9)$$

As in the previous problem, β must equal $i\lambda$. Therefore this equation reduces to

$$\sin (n + 1)\lambda - \left(2 - \frac{K_a + K_b}{k}\right)\sin n\lambda$$

$$+ \left(1 - \frac{K_a}{k}\right)\left(1 - \frac{K_b}{k}\right)\sin (n - 1)\lambda = 0 \qquad (80.10)$$

The solution of this equation can be carried out by plotting. For a given ω we have numerical values for K_a, K_b, and λ, where

$$\left.\begin{array}{l} \cos \lambda = \left(1 - \dfrac{J\omega^2}{2k}\right) \\[4mm] K_a = \dfrac{k_a}{1 - \dfrac{k_a}{J_a\omega^2}} \\[6mm] K_b = \dfrac{k_b}{1 - \dfrac{k_b}{J_b\omega^2}} \end{array}\right\} \qquad (80.11)$$

If more than one flywheel is placed on the end as shown in Fig. 118,

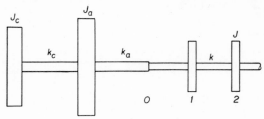

Fig. 118

J_a must be replaced by the equivalent inertia* at a, which is given by the equation

$$J_{a_{eq}} = J_a + \frac{J_c}{1 - \dfrac{J_c\omega^2}{k_c}} \qquad (80.12)$$

Problems

187. Determine the natural frequencies of a six-cylinder engine without flywheel, in terms of the fundamental.

188. If a flywheel attached at one end of an engine is very large as shown in Fig. 119, the shaft at that end can be considered to be fixed. For such a case, set up the boundary equations and show that the natural frequencies are obtained from the equation

$$\omega = 2\sqrt{\frac{k}{J}}\sin\frac{\lambda}{2}$$

where the λ's are determined from

$$\sin \lambda = 0$$
$$\cos \lambda(n + \tfrac{1}{2}) = 0$$

* W. T. Thomson, *Mechanical Vibrations*, Prentice-Hall, Inc., 1948, page 140.

189. If the flywheel of a four-cylinder engine arranged as in Fig. 119 is $J_f = 10J$, determine the natural frequencies of the system.

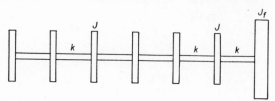

Fig. 119

81. Continuous Beams. Continuous beams of equal span can be treated by difference equations. Considering the uniformly

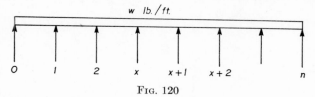

Fig. 120

loaded beam of Fig. 120, we write the three-moment-equation, which relates the moments at three adjacent supports.

$$M(x) + 4M(x + 1) + M(x + 2) = -\frac{wl^2}{2} \qquad (81.1)$$

Taking the Laplace transformation and noting that $M(0) = 0$, we obtain

$$\bar{M}(s)(1 + 4e^s + e^{2s}) = \left[M(1) - \frac{wl^2}{2(e^s - 1)} \right] \frac{e^s(1 - e^{-s})}{s}$$

$$\bar{M}(s) = \frac{M(1)\,e^s(1 - e^{-s})}{s(1 + 4e^s + e^{2s})} - \frac{wl^2}{2}\,\frac{e^s(1 - e^{-s})}{s(e^s - 1)(1 + 4e^s + e^{2s})} \qquad (81.2)$$

The quantity $(1 + 4e^s + e^{2s})$ in the denominator can be factored to $(e^s - c)(e^s - d)$, where

$$c = -2 + \sqrt{3}$$
$$d = -2 - \sqrt{3}$$
$$c - d = 2\sqrt{3}$$

It is also seen that

$$\frac{1}{(e^s - c)(e^s - d)} = \frac{1}{(c - d)} \left[\frac{1}{e^s - c} - \frac{1}{e^s - d} \right] \qquad (81.3)$$

so that the subsidiary equation becomes

$$\bar{M}(s) = \frac{M(1) e^s(1 - e^{-s})}{s(e^s - c)(e^s - d)}$$
$$- \frac{wl^2}{2(c - d)} \left[\frac{e^s(1 - e^{-s})}{s(e^s - 1)(e^s - c)} - \frac{e^s(1 - e^{-s})}{s(e^s - 1)(e^s - d)} \right] \quad (81.4)$$

From Eq. (77.14), the inverse transformation is found to be

$$M(x) = M(1) \left[\frac{c^x - d^x}{c - d} \right] - \frac{wl^2}{2(c - d)} \left[\left(\frac{1 - c^x}{1 - c} \right) - \left(\frac{1 - d^x}{1 - d} \right) \right] \quad (81.5)$$

We have already used one of the boundary equations $M(0) = 0$. We next apply the boundary equation for the right end $M(n) = 0$ and solve for $M(1)$:

$$0 = \frac{M(1)}{c - d} (c^n - d^n) - \frac{wl^2}{2(c - d)} \left[\left(\frac{1 - c^n}{1 - c} \right) - \left(\frac{1 - d^n}{1 - d} \right) \right]$$

Therefore

$$\frac{M(1)}{(c - d)} = \frac{wl^2}{2(c^n - d^n)} \left[\left(\frac{1 - c^n}{1 - c} \right) - \left(\frac{1 - d^n}{1 - d} \right) \right] \frac{1}{(c - d)} \quad (81.6)$$

Substituting back into Eq. (81.5), we get

$$M(x) = \frac{wl^2}{2(c - d)} \left[\frac{(c^n - 1)d^x - (d^n - 1)c^x}{c^n - d^n} - 1 \right] \left[\frac{1}{1 - c} - \frac{1}{1 - d} \right] \quad (81.7)$$

Noting that

$$\left(\frac{1}{1 - c} - \frac{1}{1 - d} \right) = \frac{c - d}{(1 - c)(1 - d)} = \frac{\sqrt{3}}{3}$$

we can write the final equation as

$$M(x) = \frac{wl^2}{12} \left[\frac{[(-2 + \sqrt{3})^n - 1](-2 - \sqrt{3})^x - [(-2 - \sqrt{3})^n - 1](-2 + \sqrt{3})^x}{(-2 + \sqrt{3})^n - (-2 - \sqrt{3})^n} - 1 \right] \quad (81.8)$$

Problems

190. Plot the moment at the supports of an eight-span continuous beam with uniform load, and sketch in the approximate moment variation between spans. Assume the moments at the ends to be zero.

191. If the moment at the left end of the beam of Fig. 120 is M_0, determine the moment equation at x.

192. If in Prob. 191 the uniform load is reduced to zero, determine $M(x)$.

193. For the continuous beam loaded by a concentrated load P at each mid-span, the three-moment equation becomes

$$M(x) + 4M(x + 1) + M(x + 2) = -\tfrac{3}{4}Pl$$

Determine the equation for $M(x)$ when $M_0 = M_n = 0$.

194. Set up the difference equation for the motion of the mechanical system shown in Fig. 121 and determine the general solution for the displacement of the ith mass.

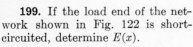

FIG. 121

195. If in Prob. 194 the ends terminate with a spring which is fixed, determine the natural frequencies.

196. In Prob. 194 show that the equations reduce to that of a uniform bar if n is increased indefinitely by subdivision.

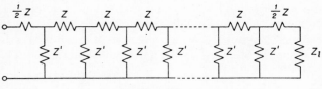

FIG. 122

197. Show that the difference equation for the electrical network shown in Fig. 122 is

$$E(x) - \left(2 + \frac{Z}{Z'}\right)E(x + 1) + E(x + 2) = 0$$

State the boundary conditions and write the general solution in terms of them.

198. Determine the steady-state output of the high pass filter of Fig. 123. Also show that there is no attenuation when $\omega^2 > 1/4LC$. What is the value of E_L/E_0 when $\omega^2 = 1/2LC$?

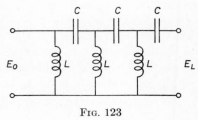

FIG. 123

199. If the load end of the network shown in Fig. 122 is short-circuited, determine $E(x)$.

200. If the load end of the network shown in Fig. 122 is open-circuited, determine $E(x)$.

CHAPTER 8

Closed-loop Systems

Servomechanisms discussed previously in the text are examples of closed-loop systems. A closed-loop system is in general an error-sensitive system. Its operation is controlled by the error between the output and the input command, and the system is continuously cognizant of the accuracy of performance.

Of great importance to the closed-loop system is the question of stability. With several elements contributing to the performance of a system, the problem of determining the stability of the system may appear formidable. Such questions, however, can be readily answered from the transfer locus plot of the system.

82. Block Diagrams. A physical system is commonly described by a schematic diagram or differential equations. The block

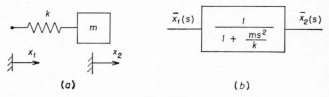

(a)   (b)

Fig. 124

diagram represents a simplified device for accomplishing the same result. In the block diagram the characteristics of an element or a component of a physical system are described by a term called *transfer function*, which is the ratio of the output to input in the subsidiary plane. In determining the transfer function, the system is assumed to be in equilibrium prior to the disturbance, and hence all initial values are taken to be zero.

EXAMPLE 82.1: Determine the transfer function of a spring-mass element and represent it by the block diagram.

With the coordinates shown in Fig. 124(a), the differential equation and its subsidiary form are

178

$$m\ddot{x}_2 = -k(x_2 - x_1) \tag{82.1}$$

$$(k + s^2 m)\bar{x}_2(s) = k\bar{x}_1(s) \tag{82.2}$$

Hence the transfer function is

$$\frac{\bar{x}_2(s)}{\bar{x}_1(s)} = \frac{k}{k + ms^2} = \frac{1}{1 + ms^2/k} \tag{82.3}$$

with the corresponding block diagram shown in Fig. 124(b).

EXAMPLE 82.2: Represent the vacuum-tube amplifier of Fig. 125(a) by a block diagram.

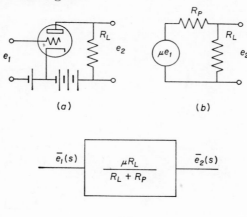

(a)   (b)

(c)

FIG. 125

The transfer function of a four-terminal network is determined with the output open-circuited. Figure 125(b) is the equivalent circuit where μ is the amplification factor and R_P is the plate resistance of the tube.* We can write the following two equations:

$$\mu e_1 = i(R_P + R_L) \tag{82.4}$$

$$e_2 = iR_L \tag{82.5}$$

With i eliminated, the transfer function is found to be a constant and is given by the equation

$$\frac{\bar{e}_2(s)}{\bar{e}_1(s)} = \frac{\mu R_L}{R_L + R_P} \tag{82.6}$$

The block diagram of the amplifier is shown in Fig. 125(c).

* See Appendix D.

83. Cascading of Elements. Two or more elements in series may be reduced to one by multiplying their transfer functions. Thus, for the system of Fig. 126, the block diagram can be represented by the transfer function of each part in series or by a single

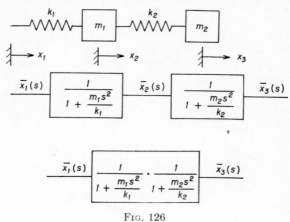

Fig. 126

block with a transfer function equal to the product of the two. The validity of this rule is easily established as follows:

$$\bar{x}_2(s) = \frac{\bar{x}_1(s)}{1 + m_1 s^2/k_1} \tag{83.1}$$

$$\bar{x}_3(s) = \frac{\bar{x}_2(s)}{1 + m_2 s^2/k_2} = \left(\frac{1}{1 + m_1 s^2/k_1} \cdot \frac{1}{1 + m_2 s^2/k_2}\right) \bar{x}_1(s) \tag{83.2}$$

In general it is feasible to combine a series of elements and to represent the transfer function of the group by a single symbol $G(s)$, as shown in Fig. 127. It should be noted that in doing so, the poles and zeros of $G(s)$ remain the poles and zeros of the individual transfer functions comprising $G(s)$. This

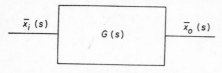

Fig. 127

fact is of considerable importance in the analysis of systems with large numbers of degrees of freedom where difficulties arise primarily in the solution of higher degree algebraic equations.

In the problem of synthesis where a desired operating characteristic is to be designed into the system, the vacuum tube offers

considerable freedom.   It is a well established fact that vacuum
tube amplifiers isolate electrical meshes; that is, the ratio of the
voltage on the grid of one tube to the grid of the preceding tube is
determined only by the amplification factor of the tube and the
network coupling the two tubes together.   This ratio may be
expressed in terms of the transfer function of the network, and the
poles and zeros of the over-all transfer function will be equal to the
poles and zeros of the individual coupling networks.

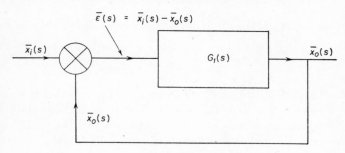

$$\bar{\epsilon}(s) = \bar{x}_i(s) - \bar{x}_0(s)$$

$\bar{x}_i(s)$

$G_I(s)$

$\bar{x}_0(s)$

$\bar{x}_0(s)$

FIG. 128

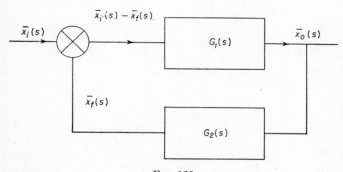

$\bar{x}_i(s) - \bar{x}_f(s)$

$\bar{x}_i(s)$

$G_I(s)$

$\bar{x}_0(s)$

$\bar{x}_f(s)$

$G_2(s)$

FIG. 129

84. Closed-Loop Analysis.   Figures 128 and 129 show two
closed-loop systems where several elements in each branch are
lumped into a single block element.   In Fig. 128 the output is fed
back directly to the differential and the error $\bar{\epsilon}(s) = \bar{x}_i(s) - \bar{x}_0(s)$
is fed to the block element.   In Fig. 129 the output is modified by
the transfer function $G_2(s)$, and the input to block 1 is the difference
between the input $\bar{x}_i(s)$ and the feed-back signal $\bar{x}_f(s)$.

Considering the system of Fig. 129, we can write the following equations:

$$\bar{x}_f(s) = G_2(s)\bar{x}_0(s) \tag{84.1}$$
$$\bar{x}_0(s) = G_1(s)[\bar{x}_i(s) - \bar{x}_f(s)] \tag{84.2}$$

Eliminating $\bar{x}_f(s)$, we obtain the output response in terms of the input command:

$$\bar{x}_0(s) = \frac{G_1(s)\bar{x}_i(s)}{1 + G_1(s)G_2(s)} \tag{84.3}$$

The response in the time domain is then obtained from the inversion

$$x_0(t) = \frac{1}{2\pi i} \int_{\gamma - i\infty}^{\gamma + i\infty} \frac{G_1(s)\bar{x}_i(s)}{1 + G_1(s)G_2(s)} e^{st} \, ds \tag{84.4}$$

85. Stability of Closed-Loop System. We shall define a system to be unstable if a disturbance, applied to it in the equilibrium state, produces an amplitude which increases without limit.

We write Eq. (84.4) in the following simplified form:

$$x_0(t) = \frac{1}{2\pi i} \int_{\gamma - i\infty}^{\gamma + i\infty} \frac{A(s) \, e^{st} \, ds}{1 + B(s)} \tag{85.1}$$

where
$$\left.\begin{array}{l} A(s) = G_1(s)\bar{x}_i(s) \\ B(s) = G_1(s)G_2(s) \end{array}\right\} \tag{85.2}$$

The value of the integral is then given by the sum of the residues, which for simple poles is

$$\sum \lim_{s \to s_i} (s - s_i) \frac{A(s) \, e^{st}}{1 + B(s)} \tag{85.3}$$

We note here that e^{st} is the only time function in this expression, and hence if any s_i has a positive real part, the system will become unstable. If the real part of all the s_i is negative, the response will decay exponentially and the system will be stable. If simple poles lie on the imaginary axis and there are no poles to the right of this axis, there will be sustained steady-state oscillation which represents the limit of stability. Finally, if an s_i coincides with the origin while all other roots are complex with negative real parts, we shall have stable oscillation, the final value of which is displaced from its initial value.

It can be shown that the same conclusions hold when there are higher-order poles in the left half plane, since for such cases the time function is in the form

$$t^n e^{s_i t} \tag{85.4}$$

For s_i with a negative real part $-a$,

$$\lim_{t \to \infty} t^n e^{-at} = 0 \tag{85.5}$$

which represents a stable function.

86. The Transfer Locus Plot of Nyquist. We have found in the previous section that instability results if a pole of the integrand lies in the right half plane. Thus, by choosing the contour shown in Fig. 130 and assuming for convenience that there are no poles on the imaginary axis, except possibly at the origin, we can express the condition for stability mathematically as

$$I = \frac{1}{2\pi i} \int_C \frac{A(s) \, e^{st} \, ds}{1 + B(s)} = 0 \tag{86.1}$$

where C is the path described.

We note here that $A(s) = G_1(s)\bar{x}_i(s)$ cannot have a pole in the right half plane, since $G_1(s)$ is a transfer function which is assumed to be stable without feedback, and $\bar{x}_i(s)$ is the transform of an input which is assumed to be regular. *Thus the only possibility for a pole in the right half plane will be due to the zero of the denominator,*

$$B(s) + 1 = 0 \tag{86.2}$$

resulting in a positive real part of s.

It is not necessary to calculate the roots of the above equation to determine whether any s has a positive real part. The methods of Hurwitz and of Routh* provide an algebraic means of establishing this point. There is also a simpler method due to Nyquist† which will also ascertain the region of the roots s and in addition will give information as to the degree of instability of the system. We shall limit our discussion only to the latter method of Nyquist.

Nyquist's criterion of stability is based on Cauchy's principle of argument (see Appendix C), which states that if a function $f(s)$ is

---

* See reference 1 at end of chapter.
† See reference 2 at end of chapter.

analytic except for poles and zeros within a closed contour, then the number of times the origin of $f(s)$ is encircled in going around the contour C is equal to the number of zeros minus the number of poles of $f(s)$, with the multiplicity of order taken into account.

$$\frac{1}{2\pi i} \int_C \frac{f'(s)\, ds}{f(s)} = N = Z - P \tag{86.3}$$

Thus to make use of this principle we can let

$$f(s) = 1 + B(s) \tag{86.4}$$

and examine the number of encirclements of the origin of $f(s)$ in traversing the contour of Fig. 130. Note now that the origin of

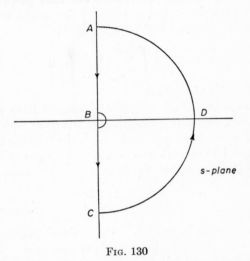

FIG. 130

$f(s)$ corresponds to $B(s) = -1$. Thus if $w = B(s)$ is plotted for the contour of Fig. 130, the number of times $B(s)$ encircles the point $w = -1 + i0$ will be equal to the number of zeros minus the number of poles of $1 + B(s)$ for s in the right half plane.

We shall now examine $w = B(s)$ along the contour of Fig. 130. Since $\lim_{s \to \infty} |B(s)| = 0$ for all physical systems with which we are concerned, points along the infinite arc CDA contract to the origin $w = 0$. Along the imaginary axis, $s = i\omega$, so that $w = B(i\omega)$.

Along the small semicircle at the origin we can let $s = \rho\, e^{i\theta}$. Since $B(s)$ is in general a rational fraction with the denominator of higher power than the numerator,

$$w = \lim_{\rho \to 0} B(\rho\, e^{i\theta}) \tag{86.5}$$

will map into a segment of an infinite circle. Thus it is necessary only to plot $B(i\omega)$ from $\omega = \infty$ to 0. Since $B(-i\omega)$ is a conjugate of $B(i\omega)$, w will be symmetric about the real axis and $B(-i\omega)$ will be the reflection of $B(i\omega)$ about the real axis of w.

Summarizing, we can write

$$I = \frac{1}{2\pi i} \int_C \frac{A(s)\, e^{st}\, ds}{1 + B(s)} = \sum \Re \tag{86.6}$$

where $\Sigma\Re$ is the sum of the residues of the integrand at the zeros of $1 + B(s)$ in the right half plane of s. The system is stable only if $Z = 0$.

Z can be determined by plotting $w = B(i\omega)$, noting the number of encirclement N of the point $w = -1 + i0$, using the equation $N = Z - P$, where P is the number of poles of $B(s)$ in the right half plane. P is in general easily found from $B(s)$ by inspection.

In single-loop systems $B(s)$ has no poles in the right half plane, and hence $Z = N$. Thus stability is ensured if the transfer locus plot $w = B(i\omega)$ does not enclose the point $w = -1 + i0$.

In multiple-loop systems $B(s)$ may have poles in the right half plane; that is, the feed-back element itself may be unstable. Thus instability is possible with $N = 0$, since $Z - P$ may be zero. Also stability is possible with $N \neq 0$, since Z may be zero and $P \neq 0$.

87. Examples in Stability. To illustrate the subject of stability, a few problems are included in this section.

EXAMPLE 87.1: Plot the Nyquist diagram and determine the stability of a closed-loop system with $B(s) = 1/1 + s$.

First we shall write $B(i\omega)$ in the form,

$$B(i\omega) = \frac{1}{1 + i\omega} = \left(\frac{1}{1 + \omega^2}\right) - i\left(\frac{\omega}{1 + \omega^2}\right)$$

Choosing various values of ω, we obtain the following table.

ω	$1 + \omega^2$	$\dfrac{1}{1 + \omega^2}$	$\dfrac{\omega}{1 + \omega^2}$	$\dfrac{1}{\omega(1 + \omega^2)}$
0	1	1	0	∞
0.20	1.04	0.960	0.192	4.80
0.60	1.36	0.735	0.441	1.23
1.00	2.00	0.500	0.500	0.500
1.40	2.96	0.338	0.473	0.241
2.00	5.00	0.200	0.400	0.100
3.00	10.0	0.100	0.300	0.033
6.00	37.0	0.027	0.162	0.0045
∞	∞	0	0	0

Using the values in this table and plotting $w = B(i\omega)$, we obtain the circle shown in Fig. 131, where the dotted portion represents

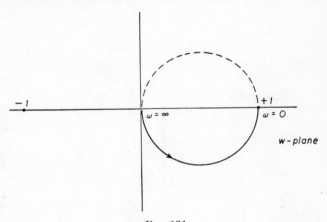

Fig. 131

$B(-i\omega)$. It should be noted here that the small semicircle at the origin of Fig. 130 contracts to the point $w = +1$. Since $B(s) = 1/(1 + s)$ has no poles in the right half plane of s and since the Nyquist diagram does not enclose the point $w = -1$, we have

$$N = P = Z = 0,$$

and the system is stable.

EXAMPLE 87.2: Determine the stability of a closed-loop system if

$$B(s) = \frac{1}{s(s - 1)}$$

Here we have a pole of the denominator $1 + B(s)$ in the right half plane; that is, $s = 1$. We therefore have $P = 1$. The pole at the origin, $s = 0$, is not included in the contour of Fig. 130, and hence it does not contribute to P.

Writing $B(i\omega)$ in the form

$$B(i\omega) = \frac{1}{i\omega(i\omega - 1)} = \frac{-1}{1 + \omega^2} + i\,\frac{1}{\omega(1 + \omega^2)}$$

we can plot the Nyquist diagram of Fig. 132 with the aid of the previous table. To determine the position of the infinite circle on

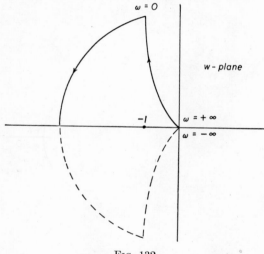

FIG. 132

the w-plane, corresponding to the small semicircle around the origin of Fig. 130, we can substitute $s = r\,e^{i\theta}$ in $B(s)$ and obtain

$$B(s) = \lim_{r \to 0} \frac{1}{r\,e^{i\theta}(r\,e^{i\theta} - 1)} \cong -\lim_{r \to 0}\left(\frac{1}{r}\,e^{-i\theta}\right)$$

Since θ goes from $\pi/2$ to $-\pi/2$, the infinite arc in the w-plane encloses the left half plane.

We see from Fig. 132 that the point $w = -1$ is enclosed once; hence $N = 1$. Solving for Z in the equation $N = Z - P$, we obtain

$$Z = N + P = 2$$

and the system is unstable.

EXAMPLE 87.3: Figure 133(a) represents an oscillator where the feedback of energy is accomplished through the coupling condenser

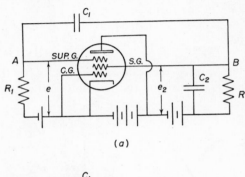

(a)

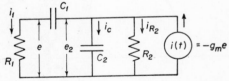

(b)

FIG. 133

C_1 between the screen and suppressor grids. With the screen potential higher than that of the plate, the secondary electrons emitted by the plate, and dependent on the control grid and plate voltages, are drawn through the screen grid. If the suppressor grid is now made positive, a part of this secondary flow is diverted through the suppressor, thus decreasing the screen current. With the control grid and plate voltages fixed, the tube can be considered to be a triode with the screen as anode and the suppressor as grid. The transconductance* of this tube $g_m = \partial i_{sg}/\partial e_g$ (between the

* See Appendix D.

screen and suppressor) is, however, negative; hence the voltages at A and B are in phase, making possible feedback through C in the proper phase relation to sustain steady oscillations.

The equivalent a-c circuit for this oscillator is shown in Fig. 133(b), where the equivalent triode is replaced by a current source $i(t) = -g_m e$ in parallel with a conductance $1/r_P$, where r_P is the resistance of the equivalent triode.* In the diagram $1/r_P$ is consolidated with R such that $R_2 = R r_P/(R + r_P)$.

Equating $i(t) = -g_m e$ to the branch currents, we have

$$-g_m e = i_1 + i_c + i_{R_2}$$
$$= \frac{e}{R_1} + C_2 \frac{de_2}{dt} + \frac{e_2}{R_2}$$

To replace e_2 by e we note that

$$e_2 = e + \frac{1}{C_1} \int_0^t \frac{e}{R_1}\, dt$$
$$\frac{de_2}{dt} = \frac{de}{dt} + \frac{e}{R_1 C_1}$$

Substituting into the current equation,

$$-g_m e = \frac{e}{R_1} + C_2 \frac{de}{dt} + \frac{C_2}{R_1 C_1} e + \frac{e}{R_2} + \frac{1}{R_1 R_2 C_1} \int_0^t e\, dt$$

Differentiating and rearranging terms,

$$\frac{d^2 e}{dt^2} + \left(\frac{1}{R_1 C_2} + \frac{1}{R_2 C_2} + \frac{1}{R_1 C_1} + \frac{g_m}{C_2} \right) \frac{de}{dt} + \left(\frac{1}{R_1 R_2 C_1 C_2} \right) e = 0$$

Since g_m is negative, it is possible to make the coefficient of the second term equal to zero, in which case we have harmonic oscillations of frequency

$$\omega = \sqrt{\frac{1}{R_1 R_2 C_1 C_2}}$$

If the coefficient of de/dt becomes negative, we obtain unstable oscillations.

* See Appendix E.

Problems

201. Determine the transfer function for the integrating circuit of Fig. 134.

202. Determine the transfer function for the coupling network of Fig. 135.

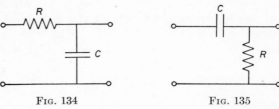

FIG. 134   FIG. 135

203. Electronic Analog computer components are commercially available to perform the following operations.

$$G(s) = \frac{1}{ks} \qquad\qquad G(s) = \left(\frac{1}{1+s}\right)^2$$

$$G(s) = \frac{1}{1+s} \qquad\qquad G(s) = \left(\frac{1-s}{1+s}\right)$$

$$G(s) = \frac{1+ks}{ks}$$

Determine the output response of these units when a unit step function is used as stimulus.

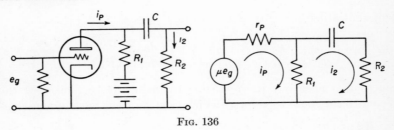

FIG. 136

204. For the vacuum tube circuit of Fig. 136, show that the equation for the transform $\bar{i}_2(s)$ for any impressed grid voltage is

$$\bar{i}_2(s) = \frac{\mu s \, \bar{e}_g(s)}{r_P \left[s\left(1 + \dfrac{R_2}{R_1} + \dfrac{R_2}{r_P}\right) + \dfrac{1}{C}\left(\dfrac{1}{R_1} + \dfrac{1}{r_P}\right) \right]}$$

If $e_g = E_0 \sin \omega t$, show that the solution is

$$i_2(t) = \frac{-\mu E_0 \omega \alpha}{\beta(\alpha^2 + \omega^2)} e^{-\alpha t} + \frac{\mu E_0}{\beta \sqrt{1 + \left(\dfrac{\alpha}{\omega}\right)^2}} \sin(\omega t + \phi).$$

where
$$\alpha = \frac{\dfrac{1}{C}\left(\dfrac{1}{R_1} + \dfrac{1}{r_P}\right)}{\left(1 + \dfrac{R_2}{R_1} + \dfrac{R_2}{r_P}\right)}, \quad \beta = r_P\left(1 + \frac{R_2}{R_1} + \frac{R_2}{r_P}\right)$$

$$\phi = \tan^{-1}\frac{\alpha}{\omega}$$

205. If a vacuum-tube amplifier consists of two stages of the circuit shown in Fig. 136, determine its transfer function. Using the solution of Problem 204, express the output voltage across the load resistor of the second stage in terms of the convolution integral.

206. Determine the transfer function and the block diagram for the torsional system shown in Fig. 137.

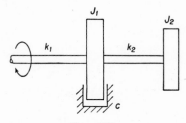

FIG. 137

207. Figure 138 shows a vacuum-tube oscillator with feed-back through the mutual inductance M. Verify the equivalent circuit and the block diagram given and show that the system will be stable if

$$\frac{R}{L} + \frac{1}{R_P C} > \frac{\mu M}{R_P C L}$$

208. Figure 139 shows an electron-coupled oscillator. Verify the block diagram given.

209. A closed-loop system has the following equation for $B(s)$.

$$B(s) = \frac{1}{s(1 + s)}$$

Plot the Nyquist diagram and show that the system is stable.

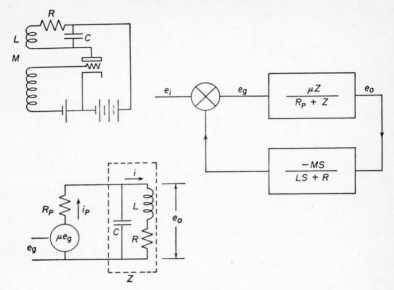

FIG. 138

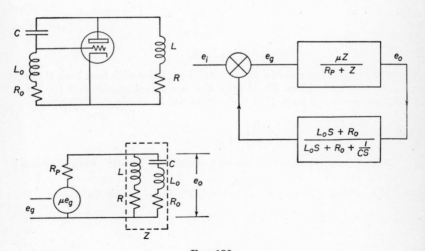

FIG. 139

210. If $B(s) = 1/(s - 2)$, show that the Nyquist diagram does not enclose the point $w = -1$, yet the system is unstable.

$Ans.$ $N = 0$, $Z = 1$, $P = 1$.

References

1. For stability criteria of Hurwitz and Routh, see Guillemin, E. A., *Mathematics of Circuit Analysis*, John Wiley, 1949, page 395. Gardner and Barnes, *Transients in Linear Systems*, John Wiley, 1942, page 197.

2. Nyquist, H., *"Regeneration Theory,"* *Bell System Tech. Jour.*, Vol. 11 (January 1932), pages 126–147.

3. MacColl, L. A., *Fundamental Theory of Servomechanism*, D. Van Nostrand, 1945.

4. Brown, G. S., and Campbell, D. P., *Principles of Servomechanisms*, John Wiley, 1948.

5. Oldenbourg, R. C., and Sartorius, H., *Dynamics of Automatic Controls*, Amer. Soc. of Mech. Engrs., 1948.

6. James, H. M., Nichols, N. B., and Phillips, R. S., *Theory of Servomechanisms*, M.I.T. Radiation Lab. Series #25.

7. Bode, H. W., *Network Analysis and Feedback Amplifier Design*, D. Van Nostrand, 1945.

CHAPTER 9
Analogies

In many cases the physical system is so complex that a direct mathematical solution by means of the differential equations is not practical or possible. For such problems, experimental methods based on analogies offer one possible approach. The system under consideration may be mechanical, electrical, acoustical, or combinations of all three. However, it is frequently possible to reduce such

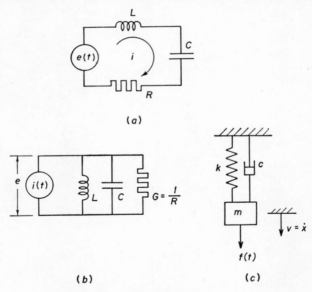

(a)

(b)

(c)

Fig. 140

a system to an analogous electrical system that may be studied experimentally. Such a study generally involves both the use of circuit theory and the principle of dimensional similarity.

88. Analogous Quantities. The analogy between systems is a mathematical one based on the similarity of differential equations.

194

For instance, the differential equations for the three systems of Fig. 140 are

$$L \frac{di}{dt} + Ri + \frac{1}{C} \int_0^t i \, dt = e(t) \tag{a}$$

$$C \frac{de}{dt} + Ge + \frac{1}{L} \int_0^t e \, dt = i(t) \tag{b}$$

$$m \frac{dv}{dt} + cv + k \int_0^t v \, dt = f(t) \tag{c}$$

which are similar in form and differ only in the letters used.

The significance of these equations is that the mechanical system of Fig. 140 can be represented by either of the two electrical circuits shown. The analogous quantities are evident from these equations and have been tabulated for convenience.

TABLE OF ANALOGOUS QUANTITIES

Mechanical Quantity		Electrical Quantity	
		Force-Voltage $(f - e)$ Analogy	Force-Current $(f - i)$ Analogy
Force (pound)	f	Voltage (volt) e	Current (ampere) i
Velocity (in./sec)	v	Current (ampere) i	Voltage (volt) e
Displacement (in.) $x = \int^t v \, dt$		Charge (coulomb) $q = \int^t i \, dt$	
Mass (lb sec²/in.)	m	Inductance (henry) L	Capacitance (farad) C
Compliance (in./lb)	$1/k$	Capacitance (farad) C	Inductance (henry) L
Resistance (lb sec/in.)	c	Resistance (ohm) R	Conductance (mho) G

89. Circuit Diagrams. Rules for setting up analogous electrical circuits are offered in this section. We shall start with the $(f - e)$ analogy, for which the following line of reasoning is required.

Force-Voltage Analogy. Springs and dashpots are in general associated with two displacements or velocities; namely, those of each end. In the case of springs, the force transmitted is proportional to the difference in the displacement of the ends, whereas the force transmitted through dashpots is proportional to the difference in the rate of change of these displacements or their velocities. The electrical analog of springs and dashpots are capacitors and resistors, which in general can be considered to have two currents flowing through them in opposite directions, as shown in Fig. 141.

The voltage across the capacitor is proportional to the difference of the charge or the time integral of the difference between the two currents, whereas the voltage across the resistor is proportional to the difference in the two currents. It is evident then that, except in cases where one end of the spring or dashpot is fixed, capacitors and resistors must be placed in a branch common to two circuits. With one end fixed, $x_1 = v_1 = 0$, which corresponds to $i_1 = 0$ or an open circuit of branch 1.

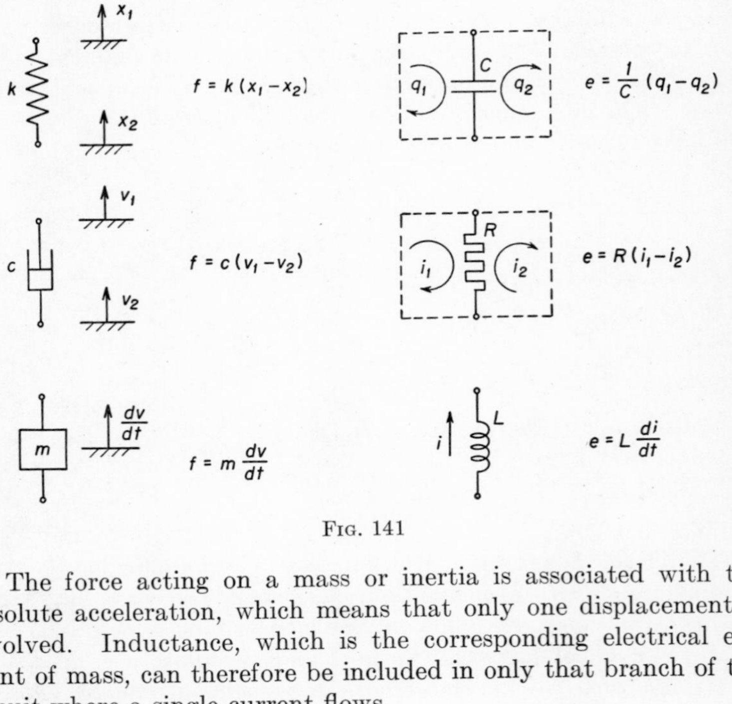

$$f = k(x_1 - x_2)$$

$$e = \frac{1}{C}(q_1 - q_2)$$

$$f = c(v_1 - v_2)$$

$$e = R(i_1 - i_2)$$

$$f = m\frac{dv}{dt}$$

$$e = L\frac{di}{dt}$$

Fig. 141

The force acting on a mass or inertia is associated with the absolute acceleration, which means that only one displacement is involved. Inductance, which is the corresponding electrical element of mass, can therefore be included in only that branch of the circuit where a single current flows.

EXAMPLE 89.1: Figure 142(a) shows a mechanical system for which an equivalent electrical circuit is desired. Using the rules given in this section, the circuit of Fig. 142(b) can be readily established as the equivalent circuit based on the $(f - e)$ analogy; that is, the inductances L_1 and L_2 corresponding to m_1 and m_2 must be associated only with single currents i_1 and i_2. The spring and dashpot k_2 and c are related to the difference of the displacement and velocity at 1 and 2; hence their equivalents C_2 and R must be placed in the branch between loop 1 and 2. Also C_3 corresponding to k_3 is placed in the branch where the difference in current $(i_3 - i_2)$ flows. The applied force being measured with respect to ground and associated with the velocity v_3, its equivalent $e(t)$ is placed in the branch with current i_3.

Force-Current Analogy. The equivalent circuit for the $(f - i)$ analogy can be obtained in two different ways. The first method

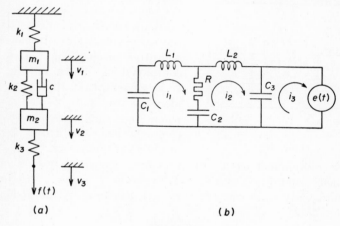

(a)   (b)

Fig. 142

assumes that the circuit diagram based on the $(f - e)$ analogy is known, from which the dual circuit of the $(f - i)$ analogy is readily obtained. In the second method, a mechanical circuit diagram is drawn. This mechanical diagram will correspond identically with the dual electrical circuit of the $(f - i)$ analogy.

We shall now illustrate both these methods for the system of example 89.1.

Method (1). From the following rules the dual electrical network can be established. We first draw the circuit for the $(f - e)$ analogy as shown in Fig. 143(a). Next place a dot in each loop and one outside; that is, a, b, c, g. These points are the nodes of the dual circuit, and the branches are established by connecting these nodes by dotted lines through each element as shown. The

dual of the elements crossed by these lines are then placed in the
respective branches of the new diagram as shown in Fig. 143(b).

Method (2). Method (2) is preferable to method (1) in that

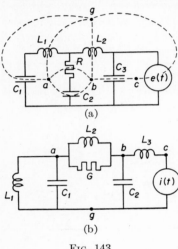

(a)

(b)

Fig. 143

the circuit diagram of the $(f - e)$
analogy is not necessary. We begin
by drawing the mechanical circuit
diagram of the system as follows.
Since masses are associated with
absolute motion, one end of each
mass must be connected to ground.
We next connect together the ends
of all mechanical elements having
the same velocity or displacement,
and the mechanical diagram is
completed as shown in Fig. 144.
It is evident that this diagram is
identical to that of Fig. 143(b)
when the analogous electrical
elements are substituted for the
mechanical quantities.

The mechanical circuit diagram is an essential feature of the
so called "mobility method" of Firestone,* which is frequently
used for steady state analysis. In fact, the mobility method makes

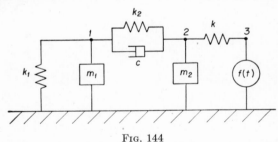

Fig. 144

use of the mechanical admittance of the elements and is comparable
to the force-current analogy.

90. The Similarity Principle. In order to determine the behavior
of a mechanical system from its equivalent electrical circuit, it is
necessary that the two systems be similar. The similarity principle

* See references 3 and 4 at end of chapter.

as set forth by Bridgman* states that the solution of a physical system must be valid in all systems of units. Thus two systems are similar if their dimensionless equations are identical. Stated in another way, a dimensionless equation must be independent of the system of units used.

As an example, the equation

$$m \frac{d^2x}{dt^2} + c \frac{dx}{dt} + kx = F_0 \sin pt \qquad (90.1)$$

can be written in the nondimensional form

$$\frac{d^2X}{dT^2} + \left(\frac{c}{m\omega}\right)\frac{dX}{dT} + \left(\frac{k}{m\omega^2}\right)X = \left(\frac{F_0}{m\omega^2 x_0}\right)\sin\left(\frac{p}{\omega}\right)T \qquad (90.2)$$

by the introduction of nondimensional variables $X = x/x_0$ and $T = \omega t$. The dimensionless equation for any similar system must be identical with respect to form and numerical values of the non-dimensional coefficients represented in the parentheses.

In general, we wish to establish the similarity between two systems without reference to their differential equations. The procedure is then to write a functional equation by fixing our attention on the particular quantity to be studied and deciding what variables could affect it. The number of dimensionless parameters in its solution is then established by Buckingham's π theorem which states that, if a physical problem has n independent variables and m fundamental units, there will be $(n - m)$ dimensionless parameters. Mechanical problems generally involve three fundamental units; namely, force, length, and time. The dimensionless parameters having been established, the corresponding quantities in the analogous system can be determined by reference to the table of analogous quantities.

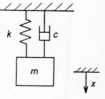

FIG. 145

EXAMPLE 90.1: Establish the dimensionless parameters for the free vibration of a damped spring-mass system of Fig. 145.

If we assume the mass to be started with displacement x_0 and velocity v_0, the displacement at any time will depend on k, m, c, x_0, and v_0. The functional equation then becomes,

$$x = f(k,m,c,x_0,v_0)$$

* Bridgman, W. P., *Dimensional Analysis*, Yale University Press, 1922.

This equation contains six independent quantities; hence by the π theorem there will be three dimensionless parameters; namely,

$$\left(\frac{x}{x_0}\right)$$

$$\left(\frac{c}{\sqrt{km}}\right) \quad \left(\frac{c}{m\omega_n}\right)$$

$$\left(\frac{v_0}{x_0\omega_n}\right)$$

where $\omega_n = \sqrt{k/m}$ is the natural frequency of the system.

EXAMPLE 90.2: Determine the dimensionless parameters for the system of Fig. 145 when a force of $F_0 \sin pt$ is applied to it.

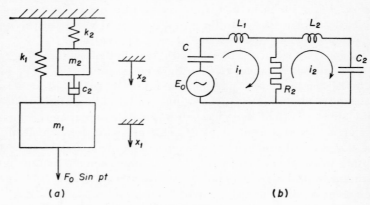

FIG. 146

Assuming the initial conditions to be zero, the functional equation becomes

$$x = f(k,m,c,F_0,p)$$

The dimensionless parameters are then

$$\left(\frac{c}{\sqrt{km}}\right)$$

$$\left(\frac{mp^2}{k}\right) = \left(\frac{p}{\omega_n}\right)^2$$

$$\left(\frac{m\omega_n^2 x}{F_0}\right) = \left(\frac{kx}{F_0}\right)$$

The dimensionless parameters obtained in Examples 90.1 and 90.2 are of basic importance to the more general problem and are tabulated with their electrical analogs in the following table.

Mechanical	Electrical	
	$f - e$ Analogy	$f - i$ Analogy
$\dfrac{p}{\omega}$	$\dfrac{p_e}{\omega_e}$	$\dfrac{p_e}{\omega_e}$
$\dfrac{mp^2}{k}$	$LC\,p_e^2$	$LC\,p_e^2$
$\dfrac{c}{\sqrt{km}}$	$R\sqrt{\dfrac{C}{L}}$	$G\sqrt{\dfrac{L}{C}}$
$\dfrac{kx}{F_0}$	$\dfrac{q}{CE_0}$	$\ldots\ldots$
$\dfrac{kv}{F_0\omega}$	$\ldots\ldots$	$\dfrac{e}{\omega Li}$

Note: p and ω are impressed and reference frequencies respectively.   It is sometimes convenient to let $\omega = \omega_n$.

The subscript e is used to differentiate between the electrical and mechanical frequencies.

EXAMPLE 90.3: For the mechanical system shown in Fig. 146(a), determine the equivalent electrical circuit and the numerical values of the electrical elements.   The constants for the mechanical system are given in the engineering units as follows:

$$k_1 = 200 \text{ lb/in.} \qquad W_1 = 300 \text{ lb}$$
$$k_2 = 20 \text{ lb/in.} \qquad W_2 = 15 \text{ lb}$$
$$c_2 = 0.10 \text{ lb-sec/in.} \qquad F_0 = 50 \text{ lb}$$
$$p = 10 \text{ rad/sec}$$

By means of the $(f - e)$ analogy, the equivalent circuit of Fig. 146(b) is readily established.   We next focus our attention on the displacement x_1 and write the following functional equation:

$$x_1 = f(k_1, k_2, m_1, m_2, c_2, F_0, p)$$

This equation indicates that the displacement x_1 is some function of the seven quantities on the right side. There are eight independent variables in this equation; hence from the π theorem there will be five dimensionless parameters as follows:

$$\frac{p}{\omega} = \frac{p_e}{\omega_e}$$

$$\frac{m_1 p^2}{k_1} = \frac{300 \times 10^2}{386 \times 200} = 0.389 = L_1 C_1 p_e^2$$

$$\frac{m_2 p^2}{k_2} = \frac{15 \times 10^2}{386 \times 20} = 0.194 = L_2 C_2 p_e^2$$

$$\frac{c_2}{\sqrt{k_2 m_2}} = \frac{0.10}{\sqrt{\frac{15}{386} \times 20}} = 0.113 = R_2 \sqrt{\frac{C_2}{L_2}}$$

$$\frac{k_1 x_1}{F_0} = 4x_1 \qquad = \frac{q_1}{C_1 E_0} = \frac{e_{c1}}{E_0}$$

The quantities on the right are the corresponding electrical parameters, which must also have the same numerical values. These relationships can be satisfied in a number of different ways. However, it will generally be necessary to choose a large value of the electrical frequency in order to limit L and C to practical values. If we let $\omega_e = 100\omega$, then

$$\frac{p}{\omega} = \frac{p_e}{100\omega}$$
$$p_e = 100p = 1000.$$

and we obtain

$$L_1 C_1 = 0.389 \times 10^{-6}$$
$$L_2 C_2 = 0.194 \times 10^{-6}$$

Letting $C_1 = C_2 = 10 \times 10^{-6}$ farads, the numerical values of the remaining quantities become

$$L_1 = 0.0389 \text{ henry}$$
$$L_2 = 0.0194 \text{ henry}$$
$$R_2 = 0.113 \sqrt{\frac{0.0194}{10 \times 10^{-6}}} = 5.0 \text{ ohms}$$

The displacement x_1 is then determined from the equation

$$x_1 = \frac{1}{4} \frac{e_{c1}}{E_0}$$

where e_{c1}/E_0 is the ratio of the voltage across the capacitor C_1 to the impressed voltage. The displacement x_2 can also be obtained in the same manner from the equation

$$x_2 = 2.5 \frac{e_{c2}}{E_0}$$

It should be pointed out that, if the electrical voltages above are obtained by means of an oscillograph, both the transient and the steady-state response will be established.

Problems

211. Figure 147 shows the essential components of a vibrometer Verify the equivalence of the circuits shown.

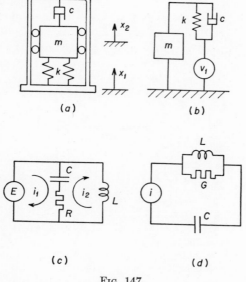

(a) (b)

(c) (d)

Fig. 147

212. Establish the analogous circuits for the mechanical systems shown in Figs. 148, 149, and 150.

213. Show by means of the $(f - e)$ analogy that the circuit diagram for the mechanical system of Fig. 151 corresponds to that of a low-pass filter.

214. Draw the mechanical circuit diagram for the system of Fig. 152. Establish the electrical circuit diagrams corresponding to the $(f - e)$ analogy and the $(f - i)$ analogy.

215. The motor shown in Fig. 153(a) is capable of translation in the vertical direction and rotation about

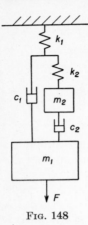

Fig. 148

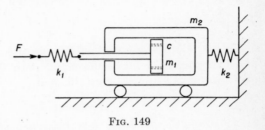

Fig. 149

its center. Show that Fig. 153(b) is its equivalent circuit where

$$L = \frac{m}{4} + \frac{J_0}{b^2}, \quad L_m = \frac{m}{4} - \frac{J_0}{b^2}, \quad C = \frac{1}{k}$$

216. The vibration absorber shown in Fig. 154 has the following constants:

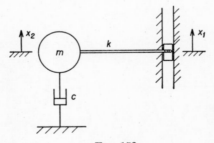

Fig. 150

$$k_1 = 500 \text{ lb/in.} \qquad W_1 = 100 \text{ lb}$$
$$k_2 = 20 \text{ lb/in.} \qquad W_2 = 10 \text{ lb}$$
$$c = 0.10 \text{ lb-sec/in.} \qquad F_0 = 5 \text{ lb}$$
$$p = 27.8 \text{ rad/sec}$$

Establish the equivalent circuit, using the $(f - e)$ analogy, and determine the numerical values of the electrical elements.

217. The following numerical values are given for the mechanical system of Fig. 155.

$$k_1 = 1000 \text{ lb/in.} \qquad W = 400 \text{ lb}$$
$$k_2 = 500 \text{ lb/in.} \qquad F_0 = 10 \text{ lb}$$
$$c = 15 \text{ lb-sec/in.} \qquad p = 10 \text{ rad/sec}$$

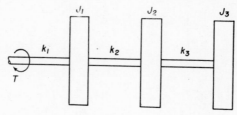

Fig. 151

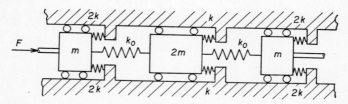

Fig. 152

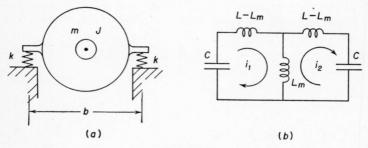

(a)   (b)

Fig. 153

Determine the numerical values for the electrical elements of the equivalent circuit for similarity of behavior. Assume 60 cps a-c voltage source and a 200 millihenry coil to be available. Indicate what measurements you would make on the electrical circuit to determine the displacements x_1 and x_2, and express these displacements in terms of these measured quantities.

218. Determine the equivalent electrical circuit for the system of Example 90.3, using the $(f - i)$ analogy. Calculate the numerical values of the electrical elements in this circuit.

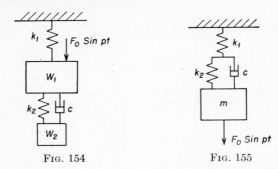

FIG. 154   FIG. 155

219. For the system of Fig. 154, discuss how you would obtain the transient response of the system to a suddenly applied impulse to W_1, giving it an initial velocity of v_0.

References

1. Gardener and Barnes, *Transients in Linear Systems*, Chapter 2.

2. Thomson, W. T., *Mechanical Vibrations*, Prentice-Hall, 1948, Chapter 8.

3. Firestone, F. A., "A New Analogy between Mechanical and Electrical Systems," *Jour. Acous. Soc. of Amer.*, Vol. 4 (1933), pages 249–267.

4. ————, "The Mobility Method of Computing the Vibration of Linear Mechanical and Acoustical Systems," *Jour. Appl. Physics*, Vol. 9 (1938), pages 373–387.

APPENDIX A

Continuity

A function $f(x)$ is continuous at the point x if for a given positive number ϵ, there exists a number δ such that for all values of h for which $|h| < \delta$, the inequality

$$|f(x + h) - f(x)| < \epsilon \tag{1}$$

is satisfied.

If in a given region δ can be found independent of x, then $f(x)$ is said to be uniformly continuous in that region.

The above definition of continuity applies also to a complex function $f(z)$ where $f(z + h) - f(z)$ is a vector difference and h is also a vector in the z plane.

The condition of continuity can also be stated in the form of a limit,

$$\lim_{h \to 0} f(x + h) = f(x) \tag{2}$$

APPENDIX B

Jordan's Lemma

If $\bar{f}(s)$ is analytic and converges uniformly to zero as s increases indefinitely, the integral along the infinite half circle is zero for $t > 0$.

$$\lim_{R \to \infty} \mathscr{E}\!\int e^{st}\bar{f}(s)\, ds = 0 \tag{1}$$

Proof: We will assume the radius of the half circle shown in Fig. 156 to be sufficiently large so that all of the poles are enclosed. Along the half circle we have,

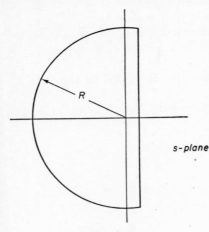

FIG. 156

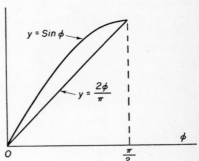

FIG. 157

$$s = R\, e^{i\theta} \qquad |s| = R$$
$$ds = iR\, e^{i\theta}\, d\theta \qquad |ds| = R\, d\theta \tag{2}$$

If $\bar{f}(s)$ is uniformly convergent, for any ϵ no matter how small, there exists an R large enough such that

$$|\bar{f}(s)| < \epsilon \tag{3}$$

We now have

$$|I(R)| \leq \int |e^{st}\bar{f}(s)\, ds| \leq R\epsilon \int_{\frac{\pi}{2}}^{\frac{3\pi}{2}} e^{Rt \cos \theta}\, d\theta \tag{4}$$

208

On substituting $\theta = \phi + \dfrac{\pi}{2}$, we obtain

$$|I(R)| \leq R\epsilon \int_0^\pi e^{-Rt \sin \phi} \, d\phi \tag{5}$$

From Fig. 157, it is apparent that the inequality

$$\sin \phi \geq \frac{2\phi}{\pi} \tag{6}$$

exists for ϕ between 0 and $\pi/2$. Also, since $e^{-Rt \sin \phi}$ is symmetric about $\phi = \pi/2$, we can rewrite Eq. (5) as

$$|I(R)| \leq 2R\epsilon \int_0^{\frac{\pi}{2}} e^{-\frac{2Rt\phi}{\pi}} \, d\phi = \frac{\epsilon\pi}{t}\left[1 - e^{-Rt}\right] \leq \frac{\epsilon\pi}{t} \tag{7}$$

As $R \to \infty$, $\epsilon \to 0$, and the integral vanishes for all $t > 0$.

References

Wagner, *Operatorenrechnung*, Edward Brothers, 1944, pages 392–393.

APPENDIX C

Cauchy's Principle of Argument

Consider an integral of the form

$$\frac{1}{2\pi i} \int_c \frac{f'(s)\,ds}{f(s)} \tag{1}$$

taken over a closed curve c. We note here that

$$\frac{f'(s)}{f(s)} = \frac{d}{ds}\left[\ln f(s)\right] \tag{2}$$

so that Eq. (1) can be rewritten as

$$\frac{1}{2\pi i} \int_c d[\ln f(s)] = \frac{1}{2\pi i}\left[\ln |f(s)| + i\phi\right]_c \tag{3}$$

Since $|f(s)|$ returns to its initial value in completing one circuit of a closed curve, the value of the integral is equal to $1/2\pi$ times the net angle ϕ swept by the radius vector from the origin to the curve c, or

$$\frac{1}{2\pi i} \int \frac{f'(s)\,ds}{f(s)} = \frac{\phi}{2\pi} = N \tag{4}$$

We know, however, that this integral is also equal to the sum of the residues at the poles of the integrand $f'(s)/f(s)$ within the curve c. It is obvious that poles of the integrand will result from the zeros of the denominator. However, poles of the integrand can also result from the poles of $f(s)$. As an example, if $f(s) = \dfrac{1}{(s-a)}$, then

$$f'(s) = -\frac{1}{(s-a)^2} \quad \text{and} \quad \frac{f'(s)}{f(s)} = -\frac{1}{(s-a)} = \pm\infty \qquad \text{at } s = a$$

Thus the value of the integral is associated with the residues at the zeros and poles of $f(s)$.

210

To establish the value of the integral for the general case, let $f(s)$ have both zeros and poles. At a zero of $f(s)$ we can write

$$f(s) = (s - a)^z \varphi(s) \tag{5}$$

where a is a zero of order z and $\varphi(s)$ a regular function not zero at a. Differentiating,

$$f'(s) = z(s - a)^{z-1}\varphi(s) + (s - a)^z\varphi'(s)$$
$$\frac{f'(s)}{f(s)} = \frac{z}{s - a} + \frac{\varphi'(s)}{\varphi(s)} \tag{6}$$

The residue of $f'(s)/f(s)$ at a is then equal to

$$\lim_{s \to a} (s - a) \left\{ \frac{z}{(s - a)} + \frac{\varphi'(s)}{\varphi(s)} \right\} = z \tag{7}$$

If there are other zeros of $f(s)$ the sum of the residues of all the zeros of $f(s)$ will be Z where multiplicity of the order of zeros is taken into account.

For the poles of $f(s)$ we can write

$$f(s) = (s - b)^{-p}\psi(s) \tag{8}$$

where b is a pole of order p and $\psi(s)$ is analytic at b. Differentiating,

$$f'(s) = (s - b)^{-p}\psi'(s) - p(s - b)^{-p-1}\psi(s)$$
$$\frac{f'(s)}{f(s)} = \frac{\psi'(s)}{\psi(s)} - \frac{p}{s - b} \tag{9}$$

and the residue of $f'(s)/f(s)$ at b becomes equal to $-p$.

We thus conclude that

$$\frac{1}{2\pi i} \int_c \frac{f'(s)\, ds}{f(s)} = \frac{\phi}{2\pi} = N = Z - P \tag{10}$$

where Z and P are zeros and poles of $f(s)$ within c with due regard for their multiplicity of order, and N the number of encirclement of the origin of $f(s)$.

References

Osgood, *Functions of a Complex Variable*, The National University of Peking Press, 1936, page 162. (See "Logarithmic Residue.")

Goursat and Hedrick, *Functions of a Complex Variable*, Ginn & Co., 1916, pages 101–102.

APPENDIX D

Equivalent Circuits of Vacuum Tubes

Since vacuum tubes are common network elements, their characteristics are briefly discussed in this section.

With the plate voltage E_P held constant as a parameter, the characteristic curves for the plate current i_P vs. grid voltage e_g will appear as shown in Fig. 158. The slope $\partial i_P / \partial e_g$ is called the trans-

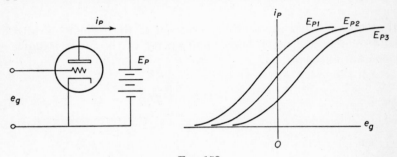

FIG. 158

conductance or mutual conductance g_m of the tube. It gives the relative change in plate current for a change in grid voltage.

The slope $\partial i_P / \partial e_P$ of the plate-current vs. plate-voltage curve is known as the plate conductance g_P, whereas its reciprocal is the plate resistance r_P. The ratio

$$\frac{g_m}{g_P} = \frac{\partial i_P / \partial e_g}{\partial i_P / \partial e_P} = \frac{\partial e_P}{\partial e_g} = \mu$$

is called the amplification factor of the tube. μ is a measure of the relative merit or gain of the tube.

To determine the equivalent circuit of a vacuum tube, we refer to Thevenin's theorem* which states that a network composed of linear elements and voltage is equivalent to a simple generator

---

* Everitt, *Communication Engineering*, 1st ed., McGraw-Hill, 1932, page 36.

with an internal impedance equal to that of the network. Thus if the range of operation of a vacuum tube is restricted to the linear portion of the curve where i_P varies linearly with e_g and e_P, the tube can be replaced by a generator of voltage μe_g with an internal

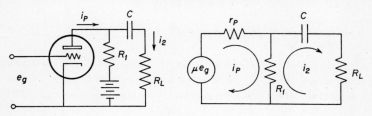

FIG. 159

resistance r_P as shown in Fig. 159. Since the battery voltage E determines only the operating region of the tube, and we are interested only in the a-c voltages and current, the d-c components need not be considered in the equivalent circuit.

APPENDIX E

Equivalent Sources

A voltage source $e(t)$ in series with a resistor R can be replaced by a current source $i(t)$ in parallel with a conductance $G = 1/R$ as shown in Fig. 160. The equivalence in the two circuits must be

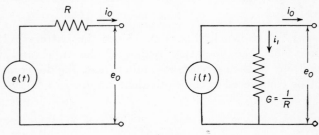

FIG. 160

established on the basis of equal terminal conditions. From the series circuit we have

$$i_0 = \frac{1}{R}\, e(t) - \frac{1}{R}\, e_0$$
$$= G\, e(t) - G\, e_0$$
$$= i(t) - i_1$$

It is obvious that the parallel circuit also satisfies the last form of this equation; hence the two circuits are equivalent. This latter form is often more convenient for networks with parallel elements, whereas the voltage source is more suitable for networks with series elements.

Reference

Bode, H. W., *Network Analysis and Feedback Amplifier Design*, D. Van Nostrand, 1945, page 12.

APPENDIX F

FUNCTIONAL OPERATIONS

$f(t)$	$\bar{f}(s)$
$f(t)$	$\displaystyle\int_0^\infty e^{-st} f(t)\, dt$
$\displaystyle\frac{1}{2\pi i}\int_{\gamma-i\infty}^{\gamma+i\infty} e^{st}\bar{f}(s)\, ds$	$\bar{f}(s)$
$f'(t)$	$s\bar{f}(s) - f(0)$
$f^{(n)}(t)$	$s^n\bar{f}(s) - s^{n-1}f(0) - s^{n-2}f'(0) - \cdots - f^{(n-1)}(0)$
$\displaystyle\int_0^t f(\tau)\, d\tau$	$\dfrac{1}{s}\bar{f}(s)$
$\displaystyle\int_0^t \int_0^\tau f(\lambda)\, d\lambda\, d\tau$	$\dfrac{1}{s^2}\bar{f}(s)$
$\displaystyle\int_0^t f_1(t-\tau) f_2(\tau)\, d\tau$	$\bar{f}_1(s) \cdot \bar{f}_2(s)$
$t f(t)$	$-\dfrac{d}{ds}\bar{f}(s)$
$\dfrac{1}{t} f(t)$	$\displaystyle\int_s^\infty \bar{f}(s)\, ds$
$f\!\left(\dfrac{t}{a}\right)$	$a\bar{f}(as)$
$e^{at} f(t)$	$\bar{f}(s-a)$

$f(t)$	$\bar{f}(s)$
$(t-a)\mathfrak{u}(t-a)$	$e^{-as}\bar{f}(s)$
$f(t) = f(t+\tau)$	$\dfrac{1}{1-e^{-\tau s}}\displaystyle\int_0^\tau e^{-rs}f(t)\,dt$
$\displaystyle\lim_{t\to 0} f(t)$	$\displaystyle\lim_{s\to\infty} s\bar{f}(s)$
$\displaystyle\lim_{t\to\infty} f(t)$	$\displaystyle\lim_{s\to 0} s\bar{f}(s)$

Jump Functions

$y(x)$	$\dfrac{(1-e^{-s})}{s}\displaystyle\sum_{r=0}^{\infty} y_r\, e^{-rs}$
$y(x+1)$	$e^s\bar{y}(s) - y_0\,\dfrac{e^s(1-e^{-s})}{s}$
$y(x+2)$	$e^{2s}\bar{y}(s) - (y_0 e^s + y_1)\,\dfrac{e^s(1-e^{-s})}{s}$
$\Delta y(x)$	$(e^s - 1)\bar{y}(s) - y_0\,\dfrac{e^s(1-e^{-s})}{s}$

APPENDIX G

TABLE OF LAPLACE TRANSFORMS

	$\bar{f}(s)$		$f(t)$
(1)	1		$\mathfrak{u}'(t) = $ unit impulse at $t = 0$
(2)	$\dfrac{1}{s}$		1 or $\mathfrak{u}(t) = $ unit step function at $t = 0$
(3)	$\dfrac{1}{s^n}$ $(n = 1, 2, \cdots)$		$\dfrac{t^{n-1}}{(n-1)!}$
(4)	$\dfrac{1}{s^{1/2}}$		$\dfrac{1}{\sqrt{\pi t}}$
(5)	$\dfrac{1}{s^{3/2}}$		$2\sqrt{\dfrac{t}{\pi}}$
(6)	$\dfrac{1}{s^n}$	$n > (0)$	$\dfrac{t^{n-1}}{\Gamma(n)}$
(7)	$\dfrac{1}{s+a}$		e^{-at}
(8)	$\dfrac{1}{s(s+a)}$		$\dfrac{1}{a}(1 - e^{-at})$
(9)	$\dfrac{1}{s^2(s+a)}$		$\dfrac{1}{a^2}(e^{-at} + at - 1)$
(10)	$\dfrac{s}{s^2 + a^2}$		$\cos at$

TABLE OF LAPLACE TRANSFORMS *(Continued)*

	$\bar{f}(s)$	$f(t)$
(11)	$\dfrac{s}{s^2 - a^2}$	$\cosh at$
(12)	$\dfrac{1}{s^2 + a^2}$	$\dfrac{1}{a}\sin at$
(13)	$\dfrac{1}{s^2 - a^2}$	$\dfrac{1}{a}\sinh at$
(14)	$\dfrac{1}{s(s^2 + a^2)}$	$\dfrac{1}{a^2}(1 - \cos at)$
(15)	$\dfrac{1}{s^2(s^2 + a^2)}$	$\dfrac{1}{a^3}(at - \sin at)$
(16)	$\dfrac{1}{(s + a)(s + b)}$	$\dfrac{1}{(b - a)}\,(e^{-at} - e^{-bt})$
(17)	$\dfrac{s}{(s + a)(s + b)}$	$\dfrac{1}{(a - b)}\,(a\,e^{-at} - b\,e^{-bt})$
(18)	$\dfrac{1}{(s + a)^2}$	$t\,e^{-at}$
(19)	$\dfrac{1}{(s + a)^n}\ (n = 1, 2, \cdots)$	$\dfrac{1}{(n - 1)!}\,t^{n-1}\,e^{-at}$
(20)	$\dfrac{s}{(s + a)^2}$	$e^{-at}(1 - at)$
(21)	$\dfrac{1}{s(s + a)^2}$	$\dfrac{1}{a^2}[1 - (1 + at)e^{-at}]$

218

TABLE OF LAPLACE TRANSFORMS (*Continued*)

	$\bar{f}(s)$	$f(t)$
(22)	$\dfrac{s+b}{(s+a)^2}$	$[(b-a)t - 1]e^{-at}$
(23)	$\dfrac{1}{(s^2+a^2)^2}$	$\dfrac{1}{2a^3}(\sin at - at\cos at)$
(24)	$\dfrac{s}{(s^2+a^2)^2}$	$\dfrac{t}{2a}\sin at$
(25)	$\dfrac{s^2}{(s^2+a^2)^2}$	$\dfrac{1}{2a}(\sin at + at\cos at)$
(26)	$\dfrac{s^2-a^2}{(s^2+a^2)^2}$	$t\cos at$
(27)	$\dfrac{1}{(s+\alpha)^2+\beta^2}$	$\dfrac{1}{\beta}e^{-\alpha t}\sin\beta t$
(28)	$\dfrac{1}{s^2+2\zeta\omega_0 s+\omega_0^2}$	$\dfrac{1}{\omega_0\sqrt{1-\zeta^2}}e^{-\zeta\omega_0 t}\sin\omega_0\sqrt{1-\zeta^2}\,t$
(29)	$\dfrac{s+\alpha}{(s+\alpha)^2+\beta^2}$	$e^{-\alpha t}\cos\beta t$
(30)	$\dfrac{1}{s[(s+\alpha)^2+\beta^2]}$	$\dfrac{1}{\omega^2}\left[1 + \dfrac{\omega}{\beta}e^{-\alpha t}\sin(\beta t - \varphi)\right]$ $\left.\begin{array}{l}\omega^2 = \alpha^2+\beta^2 \\ \varphi = \tan^{-1}\dfrac{\beta}{-\alpha}\end{array}\right\}$
(31)	$\dfrac{1}{s^2[(s+\alpha)^2+\beta^2]}$	$\dfrac{1}{\omega^2}\left[t - \dfrac{2\alpha}{\omega^2} + \dfrac{1}{\beta}e^{-\alpha t}\sin(\beta t - \varphi)\right]$ $\left.\begin{array}{l}\omega^2 = \alpha^2+\beta^2 \\ \varphi = \tan^{-1}\dfrac{2\alpha\beta}{\beta^2-\alpha^2}\end{array}\right\}$

$\bar{f}(s)$	$f(t)$
(32) $\dfrac{1}{(s^2+p^2)[(s+\alpha)^2+\beta^2]}$	$\dfrac{1}{[(\alpha^2+\beta^2-p^2)^2+4\alpha^2 p^2]^{1/2}}\left[\dfrac{1}{p}\sin(pt-\varphi_1)+\dfrac{1}{\beta}e^{-\alpha t}\sin(\beta t-\varphi_2)\right]$
	$\varphi_1=\tan^{-1}\dfrac{2\alpha p}{\alpha^2+\beta^2-p^2}\qquad \varphi_2=\tan^{-1}\dfrac{-2\alpha\beta}{\alpha^2-\beta^2+p^2}$
(33) $\dfrac{1}{s^4-a^4}$	$\dfrac{1}{2a^3}(\sinh at-\sin at)$
(34) $\dfrac{s}{s^4-a^4}$	$\dfrac{1}{2a^2}(\cosh at-\cos at)$
(35) $\dfrac{s^2}{s^4-a^4}$	$\dfrac{1}{2a}(\sinh at+\sin at)$
(36) $\dfrac{s^3}{s^4-a^4}$	$\dfrac{1}{2}(\cosh at+\cos at)$
(37) $\dfrac{s}{s^4+4a^4}$	$\dfrac{1}{2a^2}\sin at\sinh at$
(38) $\dfrac{4a^3}{s^4+4a^4}$	$\sin at\cosh at-\cos at\sinh at$
(39) $\dfrac{1}{s}\left(\dfrac{s-a}{s+a}\right)$	$-1+2e^{-at}$
(40) $\dfrac{1}{s^2}\left(\dfrac{s-a}{s+a}\right)$	$\dfrac{2}{a}-t-\dfrac{2}{a}e^{-at}$
(41) $\dfrac{e^{-as}}{s}$	$u(t-a)$

	$\bar{f}(s)$	$f(t)$
(42)	e^{-as}	$u'(t-a)$
(43)	$s\,e^{-as}$	$u''(t-a)$
(44)	$\dfrac{2}{a}e^{-a\sqrt{s}}$	$\dfrac{e^{-\frac{a^2}{4t}}}{\sqrt{\pi t^3}}$
(45)	$\dfrac{e^{-a\sqrt{s}}}{\sqrt{s}}$	$\dfrac{e^{-\frac{a^2}{4t}}}{\sqrt{\pi t}}$
(46)	$\dfrac{e^{-a\sqrt{s}}}{s}$	$1 - \text{erf}\left(\dfrac{a}{2\sqrt{t}}\right) = \text{erfc}\left(\dfrac{a}{2\sqrt{t}}\right)$
(47)	$\dfrac{1}{s\sqrt{s+1}}$	$\text{erf}\,(\sqrt{t})$
(48)	$\dfrac{1}{\sqrt{s}\,(s-1)}$	$e^t\,\text{erf}\,(\sqrt{t})$
(49)	$\dfrac{1}{\sqrt{s}+1}$	$\dfrac{1}{\sqrt{\pi t}} - e^t[1 + \text{erf}\,(\sqrt{t})]$
(50)	$\dfrac{1}{\sqrt{s^2+a^2}}$	$J_0(at)$
(51)	$\dfrac{1}{\sqrt{s^2-a^2}}$	$I_0(at) = J_0(iat)$

TABLE OF LAPLACE TRANSFORMS (Continued)

$\bar{f}(s)$	$f(t)$	
(52) $\dfrac{1}{\sqrt{s^2+a^2}+s}$	$\dfrac{1}{at}J_1(at)$	
(53) $\dfrac{1}{\sqrt{s^2+a^2}\left(\sqrt{s^2+a^2}+s\right)^n}$	$\dfrac{1}{a^n}J_n(at)$	
(54) $\dfrac{1}{s}(1-e^{-bs})$		Rectangular pulse
(55) $\dfrac{1}{b}\left(\dfrac{1-e^{-bs}}{s}\right)^2$		Triangular pulse
(56) $\dfrac{a}{s^2+a^2}\left(1+e^{-\frac{\pi s}{a}}\right)$		Sinusoidal pulse
(57) $\dfrac{1}{s}\tanh\left(\dfrac{as}{2}\right)$		Meander function

	$\bar{f}(s)$		$f(t)$
(58)	$\left[\dfrac{1}{as^2} - \dfrac{e^{-as}}{s(1 - e^{-as})}\right]$	Saw tooth wave	
(59)	$\dfrac{1}{s^2}\tanh\dfrac{as}{2}$	Triangular wave	
(60)	$\dfrac{a}{(s^2 + a^2)\left(1 - e^{-\frac{\pi s}{a}}\right)}$	Half-wave rectification of sine wave	
(61)	$\dfrac{a}{s^2 + a^2}\coth\dfrac{\pi s}{2a}$	Full-wave rectification of sine wave	

TABLE OF LAPLACE TRANSFORMS (Continued)

Jump Functions

	$\bar{f}(s)$	$f(t)$
(62)	$\dfrac{c}{s}$	c
(63)	$\dfrac{e^s}{(e^s-1)^2}\dfrac{(1-e^{-s})}{s}$	x
(64)	$\dfrac{e^s(e^s+1)}{(e^s-1)^3}\dfrac{(1-e^{-s})}{s}$	x^2
(65)	$\dfrac{e^s(e^{2s}+4e^s+1)}{(e^s-1)^4}\dfrac{(1-e^{-s})}{s}$	x^3
(66)	$\dfrac{e^s}{e^s-c}\cdot\dfrac{(1-e^{-s})}{s}$	c^x
(67)	$\dfrac{e^s}{(e^s-c)(e^s-d)}\dfrac{(1-e^{-s})}{s}$	$\dfrac{c^x - d^x}{c - d}$
(68)	$\dfrac{e^s\sinh\beta}{e^{2s}-2e^s\cosh\beta+1}\dfrac{(1-e^{-s})}{s}$	$\sinh\beta x$
(69)	$\dfrac{e^s\sin\beta}{e^{2s}-2e^s\cos\beta+1}\dfrac{(1-e^{-s})}{s}$	$\sin\beta x$
(70)	$\dfrac{e^s(e^s-\cosh\beta)}{e^{2s}-2e^s\cosh\beta+1}\dfrac{(1-e^{-s})}{s}$	$\cosh\beta x$
(71)	$\dfrac{e^s(e^s-\cos\beta)}{e^{2s}-2e^s\cos\beta+1}\dfrac{(1-e^{-s})}{s}$	$\cos\beta x$

APPENDIX H

Bibliography

HISTORICAL

1. Heaviside, O., *Electrical Papers* (2 vols.), The Macmillan Co., New York and London, 1892.

2. Heaviside, O., *Electromagnetic Theory* (3 vols.), The Electrician Printing & Publishing Co., London, 1894, 1899, and 1912. Reprinted by Benn Brothers, London, 1922.

3. Bromwich, T., "Normal Coordinates in Dynamical Systems," *Proc. London Math. Soc.*, Ser. 2, **15** (1916), pages 401–448.

4. Wagner, K. W., "Über eine Formel von Heaviside zur Berechnung von Einschaltvorgängen," *Arch. für Elektrotechnik*, **4** (1916), pages 159–193.

5. Carson, J. R., "On a General Expansion Theorem for the Transient Oscillations of a Connected System," *Phys. Rev.*, Ser. 2, **10** (1917), pages 217–225.

6. Carson, J. R., "Theory of the Transient Oscillations of Electrical Networks and Transmission Systems," *Trans. Amer. Inst. of Elect. Engrs.*, **38** (1919), pages 345–427.

7. Levy, P., "Le Calcul Symbolique d'Heaviside," *Bull. des Sciences Mathematique*, **50** (1926), pages 174–192.

8. March, H. W., "The Heaviside Operational Calculus," *Bull. Amer. Math. Soc.*, **33** (1927), pages 311–318.

9. Van der Pol, B., "A Simple Proof and Extension of Heaviside's Operational Calculus for Invariable Systems," *Philosophical Mag.*, Ser. 7 (1929), pages 1153–1162.

10. Doetsch, G., *Theorie und Anwendung der Laplace-Transformation*, Dover Publ., 1943 (see page 426).

11. Higgins, T. J., "History and Present State of the Operational Calculus as Applied in Electric Circuit Analysis," *Electrical Engineering*, **68** (Jan. 1949), pages 42–45 (contains 84 references to subject).

GENERAL

12. Churchill, R. V., *Modern Operational Mathematics in Engineering*, McGraw-Hill Book Co., 1944.

13. Gardner, M. F., and Barnes, J. L., *Transients in Linear Systems*, John Wiley & Sons, 1942.

14. Goldman, S., *Transformation Calculus and Electrical Transients*, Prentice-Hall, 1949.

15. Carslaw, H. S., and Jaeger, J. C., *Operational Methods in Applied Mathematics*, 2nd Ed., Oxford Univ. Press, 1947.

16. McLachlan, N. W., *Complex Variable and Operational Calculus*, The Macmillan Co., 1946.

17. Wagner, K. W., *Operatorenrechnung*, Edwards Brothers, 1944.

18. Doetsch, G., *Theorie und Anwendung der Laplace-Transformation*, Dover Publications, 1943.

19. Karman, T., and Biot, M. A., *Mathematical Methods in Engineering*, Chapter 10, McGraw-Hill Book Co., 1940.

20. Pipes, L. A., *Applied Mathematics for Engineers and Physicists*, Chapter 21, McGraw-Hill Book Co., 1946.

21. Doetsch, G., *Tabellen zur Laplace-Transformation*, Springer-Verlag in Berlin, Univ. of Gottingen, 1947. (Most complete table on Laplace Transformation.)

Index

J

L

M

N

O

P

R

S